ONE WORLD OF SCIENCE

Publication Number 650
AMERICAN LECTURE SERIES®

A Monograph in
The BANNERSTONE DIVISION *of*
AMERICAN LECTURES IN THE HISTORY OF MEDICINE AND SCIENCE

Edited by
WIKTOR W. NOWINSKI, Ph.D. (Cantab.), Dr. Phil. (Berne)

Research Professor of Biochemistry
Director, Cell Biology Unit
Department of Surgery
The University of Texas, Medical Branch
Galveston, Texas

ONE WORLD
OF SCIENCE

Personal Visits to Men of Research in Many Lands

By

WARREN ANDREW, Ph.D., M.D.

Chairman, Department of Anatomy
Indiana University Medical School
Indianapolis, Indiana

CHARLES C THOMAS • PUBLISHER
Springfield • Illinois • U.S.A.

Published and Distributed Throughout the World by
CHARLES C THOMAS • PUBLISHER
Bannerstone House
301-327 East Lawrence Avenue, Springfield, Illinois, U.S.A.
Natchez Plantation House
735 North Atlantic Boulevard, Fort Lauderdale, Florida, U.S.A.

© *1966, by* CHARLES C THOMAS • PUBLISHER
Library of Congress Catalog Card Number 66-14252

With THOMAS BOOKS careful attention is given to all details of
manufacturing and design. It is the Publisher's desire to present books
that are satisfactory as to their physical qualities and artistic possibilities
and appropriate for their particular use. THOMAS BOOKS will be true
to those laws of quality that assure a good name and good will.

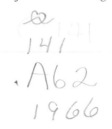

Printed in the United States of America
X-2

FOREWORD

A DESIRE for knowledge has been linked, in many instances, with a strong urge to travel over the world and among men of many countries and types of vocation. Indeed, the unquenchable thirst for understanding, for the accumulation and comparison of facts, led even Plato and Aristotle on journeys to distant parts of the ancient world, and Herodotus collected many of the materials for his great *History* at first hand in the nations of which he wrote.

Such a wanderlust seems most fitting in men whose studies must profit by wide travel. Scholars, such as Alexander von Humboldt, pursuing his inquiries into the nature of earth and cosmos in his travels from the great rivers of Spanish America and the lofty peaks of the Andes to the frozen tundras of Siberia, or Alexander Agassiz, cruising to the Galapagos or across the Indian Ocean to plumb the depths of the sea and explore the mysteries of its manifold life are among those fortunate men who have been able to follow the call of knowledge and of physical, as well as intellectual, adventure.

Yet there seems to be an element in the urge to go and to see which is of a deeply symbolic nature for the seeker after knowledge and which often is not susceptible of a strictly rational and empirical explanation.

When Paracelsus, filled with the burning desire for learning and achievement, is about to set out upon a quest over the face of the earth, his friend, Festus, remonstrates with him:

> What books are in the desert? Writes the sea
> The secret of her yearning in vast caves
> Where yours will fall the first of human feet?

But Paracelsus does set out, and we cannot but feel that Browning intended that the reader would feel these *two* desires, for knowledge and for travel, as reinforcing each other.

As one of the great number of individuals engaged in the search for scientific truth in this mid-portion of the twentieth century, my own place of work has rightfully been in the laboratory, and usually seated at a microscope, whether the light microscope, with its magnification of some one thousand times in my earlier studies, or, as more recently, the electron microscope, with an enlarging power of one million times. True, this "world" should be large enough—but ever and again has come the quiet but insistent wondering, "What is it like over in . . .?" And with this has come a curiosity linked with the profound admiration for the achievements of scientists of many countries.

These are the reasons why, whenever there has seemed to be a possibility, even a remote one, of travelling to a distant country, of visiting the laboratory, and perhaps the home, of a scientist in that country, I have not hesitated to do everything possible to make the hope a reality.

It is the accounts of some of these visits, chiefly to scientists whose names are very well known to their fellows, and in many cases, to all mankind, which are contained in this book.

How was the book written? Very early in our travelling experiences, I was made aware of the kaleidoscopic nature of the impressions which impinge upon one in strange surroundings, amid scenes which constantly are shifting, and in the meetings with new friends and with men whose names we long have known but whom we now see face to face. The natural way to prevent the loss or confusion of the precious experiences has been followed by so many in the past: the keeping of a journal. Here the happenings, the words, the fleeting impressions have been recorded from day to day and even hour to hour.

But since, when we planned the book, we felt a need for some additional information about each of the scientists whom we had visited, a phase of correspondence followed in which our friendships, made at first hand, were strengthened, and in which our information was fortified with some added factual material about the life and work of each.

The accounts represent a span of some twenty-two years, from 1940 to 1962 (there have been other travels since). They are not in chronological order. While the approximate time may be told in some cases by reference to the political situation in a particular country or to the general state of world affairs, it does not in itself seem to us to be of importance. To satisfy any possible desire of the reader to know, however, we may list here the numbers of the narratives in the order in which the visits were made: 1940, *10;* 1941, *12;* 1942, *11;* 1945, *7;* 1945-'46, *2;* 1949, *5* and *6;* 1952, *1;* 1954, *4, 8,* and *9;* 1955, *3;* 1957, *14;* 1960, *13* and *15,* and 1962, *16* and *17.*

On most of the journeys, and on some of the visits, my wife, also an investigator and, incidentally, a very good traveller, accompanied me. She is the "Nancy" of the narratives.

W.A.

Dedicated to

Edmund Vincent Cowdry

Whose Broad Vision, Encouragement
and Inspiration have helped the
author to think of this globe as
One World of Science

CONTENTS

ONE WORLD OF SCIENCE

Doctor Warren Andrew with Doctor Harish Chandra Srivastava at the doorway of a Jain Temple in Jamnagar, India.

Chapter 1

MONKEYS, MICROBES AND A MAN

A Visit to Doctor Herbert C. Clark,
Director of the Gorgas Memorial
Institute of Tropical Medicine

IT SEEMS a long way indeed from the wide avenues and
stately buildings of Washington, D.C., to the jungles of
Panama, but our capital city is like the hub of a giant wheel

FIGURE 1   Herbert Clark.

3

whose spokes reach far out into many regions of the world.

One spring day I left my office at the George Washington University and took a taxi to the Pan-American Union. I had been invited to attend the annual meeting of the W. C. Gorgas Memorial Institute of Tropical Medicine. The invitation had come from the president of the institute, Doctor Joseph Siler. It had been the result of a luncheon conversation with Doctor Alexander Wetmore, a scholar of note and a student of the bird life of Panama, a country to which he had made many expeditions. At that time he was the secretary of the Smithsonian Institute. We had found that we had a common interest in travel in Latin America, and he had suggested that I would like to hear more at first hand of the medical and biological work of the Institute of Tropical Medicine.

The meeting was held in one of the council chambers of the union. The high-backed chairs about the long table each bore a name and emblem of one of the countries of Latin America, although the membership of the Institute, of course, is not along these lines.

The first reports, concerning budget and such other necessary, but more prosaic, matters, passed somewhat slowly. But when the president introduced the main speaker, the atmosphere changed immediately. For here was the "man on the scene"— the director of the laboratories in Panama—the "old man" of American tropical medicine—Doctor Herbert Charles Clark. It was a surprise—to me, at least, who had not seen him before—to realize that this man, rugged and full of energy, had passed his seventieth birthday. Short, but sturdy, with flashing blue eyes and handsome white hair, he looked fully capable, as we knew that he was, of long and arduous treks in the jungles of Central America.

His report, illustrated with a map of Panama and with slides, made, for me, a fascinating hour.

Our introduction after the meeting brought me into only brief contact with him, for there were many who wished to avail themselves of his rather short visit to Washington.

It was later that the idea began to grow on me that both

our medical and biological interests would profit greatly if we—
somehow—could visit the Institute and even some of the wilderness country of Panama which Doctor Clark had described so
vividly.

"The wish is father to the deed." A few months had passed,
and here we were. We had flown into Panama City from Miami
on the previous day and were staying at the well-known old
Tivoli Hotel. Our plans were to spend a few days in the City,
to obtain some firsthand acquaintance with the Gorgas Institute
of Tropical Medicine and then to proceed to Barro Colorado
Island, a biological Mecca where the primitive rain forest,
with all of its plant and animal life, had been left undisturbed
and made accessible for scientific study only.

This morning we were to visit the Institute. Doctor Clark
would not reach the laboratory until some time after ten o'clock
(he had just become a grandfather, and plans were on hand for
a christening). Our time, therefore, was leisurely. After breakfast in the spacious dining room—spacious does not here imply
luxury but a knowledge of how to build in the Tropics—we
strolled awhile in the garden. There were many varieties of
tropical plants, and a huge old mimosa tree dominated the scene.

The Institute is at some distance from our hotel, which was
near the center of the city, and we took a taxi to it. It is on a
broad and beautiful avenue, Avenida Arosomane. As we walked
toward the door, we saw the sign, in Spanish, which announced
that here we were—actually about to enter the Gorgas Memorial Institute of Tropical Medicine. A brown-skinned attendant met us and led us to the office of our host. Doctor Herbert
Clark, in his long white laboratory coat, looked little different
from the way I had remembered him, except, perhaps, more
in place, more perfectly suited to the environment. He was all
cordiality and yet most businesslike, for he began very soon to
explain to us in more detail the organization of the work at the
Institute and also the nature of the place for which we soon
would be embarking.

Many able investigators have worked at the Gorgas Institute,
but Herbert Clark seemed to be the very genius and spirit of

the place. Indeed, this was not too surprising, for, since its founding in 1929, he had served as its director and had worked diligently in laboratory and jungle to further the knowledge of tropical disease and the means of its control.

The W. C. Gorgas Institute was established as a memorial to that other great physician, William Crawford Gorgas, the conqueror of yellow fever. This dread illness came sharply to the attention of United States Army authorities during and just after the Spanish-American War. When Cuba and Puerto Rico had been occupied, Colonel Gorgas, already a student of the disease, which in the nineteenth century took many lives in fearful epidemics in our own country, was sent to Havana.

The early efforts of Colonel Gorgas in Havana led to a remarkable cleaning up of the city, until that time a filthy community. But oddly enough, this cleanup did not decrease the incidence of yellow fever. The piece of the puzzle which was lacking was a very important one—the cause of the disease!

For twenty years, Doctor Carlos J. Finlay of Cuba had insisted that the carrier of the disease was a particular type of mosquito—the Stegomyia (Aedes aegypti of the present day). Now, with the United States Army on the job, there was going to be an opportunity for this theory to be proved true or false. The Surgeon General appointed a commission of four men, including Walter Reed, after whom our great army hospital in Washington is named. The members of this commission actually experimented on themselves. With such heroic work, and with the aid of volunteer soldiers, they proved beyond any reasonable doubt that the Stegomyia, a "household" type of mosquito, does indeed carry the parasite of yellow fever.

Now Colonel Gorgas, armed with knowledge, the mightiest of weapons, set out to destroy all of the mosquitoes of this type in and near Havana. The details of his methods are told in other places. It is sufficient to say that with true military precision he divided the area into districts, sought out and destroyed or made ineffective the breeding-places of the mosquitoes, screened many of the houses and maintained a constant survey of houses, water containers, puddles and drainage.

The amazing result of his campaign was the nearly complete eradication of the disease from a city which had had some cases present every day of the year for almost 150 years!

Colonel Gorgas, then, was the logical person to look to when the United States took up the tremendous task of completing the Panama Canal, a task from which the French had retreated under the attacks of yellow fever. In this strip of swamp and jungle country, fifty miles in length and ten in width, Colonel Gorgas and yellow fever again came to grips. For a second time, using many of the methods found successful in Havana and some adapted specifically to the new type of terrain, Colonel Gorgas triumphed. In this triumph, he undoubtedly saved thousands of lives, and it is likely that without such work the canal itself would not have been brought to completion.

It was wholly fitting, therefore, that the Institute be named after Doctor Gorgas. But long before the founding of the Institute, Herbert Clark, as a recent graduate of the School of Medicine at the University of Pennsylvania, had gone to Panama to work under Doctor Gorgas. The latter had been looking for a pathologist, and Doctor Clark, who had a considerable interest in this field, felt that some months in the Tropics would add to his experience. He little realized that those months would lengthen into a period of over forty years!

Doctor Clark told us that those early times in Panama proved how much interest the Tropics could hold for him. In addition to his regular work, he and some associates would ride out along the old *Camino Real,* the "Royal Road," by which the Spaniards would cross the Isthmus. Here Herbert would engage in his hobby of orchid-hunting, climbing high into the jungle trees in search of the exotic blossoms. In the first few years in Panama, he sent back over 1,500 specimens of them to horticultural gardens in our country.

Two stories which we heard of these expeditions show that "flower-picking" of this type was far from being an effete occupation. On one occasion, Herbert, high in a tree, grasped what he thought was a vanilla vine—and it was a brilliant green snake! On another occasion, again high among the branches, he was set upon by fire-ants, which merit their name by the effect of their bites; he chose retreat as the best policy and jumped into a stream thirty feet below!

Doctor Clark has collected thousands of specimens of snakes in Central America. These have been contributed to the Harvard Museum of Comparative Zoology. They include the deadly fer-de-lance and the dreaded bushmaster.

If you comment on the bravery of a jungle-trekker such as Doctor Clark in relation to poisonous snakes, he will remind you that the chances of receiving a fatal bite from one of these creatures in the field are about the same as the chances of being struck by lightning.

Doctor Clark, after a little of this type of delightful reminiscing, said, "let us take a little tour of the Institute, and you can see some of the problems which interest us at present." We went out through a rear door onto grounds which surprised us by their spaciousness. Here sheep were grazing peacefully, apparently undisturbed by their role as experimental animals. Some large cages contained two varieties of spider monkeys—red and black. "There is some question," Doctor Clark told us, "as to whether these varieties interbreed in nature, but we know that they have done so in our cages." Farther on were some Indian macacques, big husky fellows who seemed not too pleased by our presence. "These boys," Doctor Clark said, "are inclined to be pretty vicious."

We returned to the laboratories and now entered a small, but important, room—the insectary. Here, well-screened, but nevertheless looking somewhat menacing, were swarms of mosquitoes. "These," said Doctor Clark, "are specimens of the species Anopheles abu-manus. They are distinguished by wedge-shaped bodies and some other features." We knew enough to recall that Anopheles is the carrier of the malarian protozoan, but our knowledge did not extend to individual species of the genus. "This may interest you," Doctor Clark said, and led us over to a tank of water. It was alive with wrigglers! These are the aquatic larvae or young of the mosquitoes. Several microscopic slides, thin slips of glass about one inch wide by three inches long, were floated by corks at the surface of the water. They were coated with some thick creamy material. Our curiosity must have been visible, for Doctor Clark smiled as we looked at these unconventionally used slides. "Those," he said, "are the 'milk-bottles' for our baby mosquitoes. The slides are covered with yeast, which seems to make an excellent diet for these little larvae." Satisfied on this point, it occurred to me to ask, "What do the adult mosquitoes eat here in the laboratory?" "Bananas," was the laconic reply, but any picture of a mosquito peeling a banana was soon dispelled, as Doctor Clark explained that the adult used its proboscis to suck up the juices and that from the fermenting fruit it probably also obtained yeast cells.

In the laboratories within the building we also saw cages with monkeys. One was a young howler. Later we were to be thrilled by the reverberating cries of these howlers in their true jungle environment. Another was a delicate looking night-monkey with large eyes—a really charming creature.

Doctor Clark now arranged for us to visit with several of the scientists at the Institute in their individual laboratories. Among these was Doctor Fairchild, a devoted worker on the biting insects of the tropics. From our talks with Doctor Fairchild and others we learned some interesting personal items about Doctor Clark's way of working. He has made himself most popular among the natives in the little villages of the interior. In a *cayuco*, a native "dugout canoe," driven by a struggling motor, he carries his drugs and his scientific equipment to test the blood for malaria or other diseases. As he beaches, a scene of really spontaneous welcome is enacted. All the villagers who can move come down to greet him—men with filed teeth and hair in bangs, women with great rings in their ears, and a host of naked children rush toward him. Many he calls by name. Men and women are greeted with easy familiarity, and he is like a kindly granddaddy to the naked children. He obtains specimens of blood from the earlobes, first of the children, then the women and last the men. These are for spreading upon slides, where they will be closely studied under the micro-

FIGURE 2   Hideyo Noguchi, noted for his studies on yellow fever. A sculptured bust at the Rockefeller Institute for Medical Research. (Reproduced by kind permission of the Institute.)

scope for detection of the malaria parasite, a tiny one-celled animal which goes through a complicated life history, largely within the red blood corpuscles of its human host.

Early in the history of the Gorgas Institute, Doctor Clark set up a series of nine experimental villages along the Chagres River and close to the center of the Isthmus. Here, at that time, over 60 per cent of the natives showed the malaria parasite in their blood. By 1951, only about one per cent showed such parasites!

It has not always been easy to persuade the natives to take their medicine. When the doctor ran into some particularly stubborn attitudes in this regard, he hit upon a very interesting method of increasing the attractiveness of the medicine. There had been a popular pink pill in these regions for some years. It was supposed to make the men more manly and the members of the fair sex more ardent. He imitated this pill, but put in his therapeutic quantities of quinine, iron and strychnine. The natives gobbled up these new pink pills, and down went the incidence of malaria.

The old enemy of man in the Tropics had not yet been wholly beaten. In 1949, some cases of a disease which few could identify appeared in Santo Tomás Hospital in Panama City. Doctor Clark examined the tissue slides from those who came to autopsy. There could be no mistake—it was the dreaded yellow jack which had killed so many in earlier years! Here was a potentially terrible danger for the peoples of tropical America. The scientific laboratories went to work immediately to seek the source from which the virus was arising. At the Gorgas Memorial Institute in Panama, the Carlos Finlay Institute in Bogotá, Colombia, and in the Servicio Nacional de Febre Amarela in Rio de Janeiro, Brazil, men worked systematically and diligently.

It was Hideyo Noguchi, a Japanese microbiologist with the Rockefeller Institute for Medical Research, who had discovered the causative agent of yellow fever in 1918. He prepared a preventive vaccine and a curative serum for the disease. On an expedition to British West Africa in 1928, he himself fell, a victim to the dread fever.

The virus was found in the blood of monkeys and other animals. To Clark and his coworkers, one of the great questions was, "How far north does the disease now exist?" In 1951 they made an expedition to Chiapas, Mexico. Here they not only found the disease to be endemic, but two young entomologists who accompanied Clark apprehended the guilty carrier—in this case, not the town dweller, Aedes aegypti, but a treetop mosquito which became dangerous usually only when trees were felled!

The trip to Chiapas was only a portion of the jungle trekking which Herbert Clark carried out in the attempts to detect yellow fever in its animal reservoirs and to prevent its spread. He surveyed the monkeys, sloths, squirrels, ocelots, porcupines, peccaries and anteaters from Colombia on the east to Costa Rica on the west—and all this at an age when many men have retired to the easy chair!

Clark appeared at the door of the laboratory where we were talking with his colleagues. He told us that his car was at our disposal to take us back to our hotel. Since we still had preparations to make before leaving for our jungle island of Barro Colorado, we decided to go on. "When you return to Panama City," Clark told us, "we shall see you again."

* * *

It was about two weeks later that we saw Clark for the second time. We had returned from Barro Colorado with a good collection of scientific specimens and a much increased knowledge of the tropical rain forest. When Herbert Clark greeted us this time at the Institute, we acted and spoke, I am afraid, as though we were much more experienced than we had a right to feel. In any event, and perhaps because he had entertained other "tenderfeet," he did not minimize our two weeks in an environment in which he had spent forty years. After listening to our account of our own experiences in jungle trekking and collecting, he invited us to join him at a dinner party.

That evening at Panama's famous old Union Club was a delightful occasion. Two other visiting scientists, a man and wife whom we had met previously, Clark, his daughter and her husband were present. We had our martinis inside the club, but for our dinner we sat on the open terrace, with a starlit sky above and a magnificent panorama of the harbor and city stretched before us. It was here, as we lingered over our crème de menthe, that Herbert Clark told us a little of his earlier life. During the First World War he had been assigned to study the pathological effects of poison gas and sent to Paris to carry out his mission. "It was a necessary job, but hardly an appealing one," he said, "and you may be sure that I was glad to return to the Tropics when the war was over."

I asked him in what accomplishments he felt most satisfaction. Although he has published over one hundred papers, he frequently tends to minimize his work or to see it chiefly as a part of a larger whole. "I suppose," he said, "that my work with a protozoan disease of horses here has given me about as much satisfaction as a man should take in his own work. You see, the vector, or carrier, of the protozoan, a trypanosome, was unknown. Usually one thinks of an insect in such cases, such as the mosquito for malaria and yellow fever and the tsetse fly for sleeping sickness. Well, I was able to show that in *this* case the culprit is a mammal—the vampire bat!"

As I talked with Clark, handsome in his white suit, with his bronzed kindly features, clear blue eyes and eager intellectual attitude, I could not help contrasting him with the picture of the white man in the Tropics which we so often are given in the writings of fiction—a degenerate, apathetic character slouched over his glass of spirits. After all, I reflected, it is still the inner drive which counts. To a man like Clark, the Tropics have meant a home, a laboratory and a lifetime challenge!

Chapter 2

MI AMIGO

A Visit to Professor Julio María Sosa in Montevideo

"**F**LYING DOWN TO RIO" was a lively tune which made a pleasant impression on me when I was a graduate student at Yale. Later, when I had traveled into Latin America on

FIGURE 3 Julio María Sosa.

14

visits to Mexico and Guatemala, my desire to go some day to Rio
and other exotic places on the great continent to the south became a very tangible feeling. Still, if it had not been for one
man, it is more than likely that I would not have had the opportunity to satisfy that desire. That one man—Julio María Sosa
—I shall think of always as "mi amigo."

Among some of the earliest reprints of scientific papers which
I received as a young instructor were certain beautifully illustrated ones from Montevideo, Uruguay. I admired the exquisite details of the drawings well before the name itself—
Sosa—impressed itself on my mind. So it was that one day at
an anatomical meeting at Northwestern University, I was surprised when a close acquaintance told me, "Doctor Sosa would
like to meet you." In fact, I was so unprepared that I actually
thought he had said, "Doctor so-and-so wants to meet you"!

As we talked, Julio María was approaching us. The best words
to describe him, and rather strange words to describe a scientist,
were dashing and cavalier. There was an air of lively animation,
of eager enthusiasm which literally radiated from his person.
His features, sharp and cleancut, were accentuated by the trim
black mustache and the sleek black hair. The slight roundness
of his figure seemed to hinder in no way the quickness and
agility of his motion. "Doctor Andrew," he said, "I am enchanted. I have long hoped to meet you."

What was a Uruguayan doing here at a regional meeting of
the anatomists in Chicago? I soon learned that Sosa was spending a number of months in the United States and at this time
was working with the renowned scientist, Professor R. R.
Bensley, at the University of Chicago. "To all of us at the
laboratory he is 'Papa Bensley'—I love him," Julio María said
with great fervor. "He is a really great man." His high regard
was particularly impressive, since he was so versed in the classical methods of staining and the work of the Spanish school,
while Bensley was the pioneer of physical methods in cytology—
the breakdown of the cells into their parts by very modern
techniques such as high-speed centrifugation. Doctor Sosa told
me that he had brought with him to the States his wife, Isabel,

and little boy, Carlito. "You must meet them," he said, and
since the formal meeting had ended, I agreed to go with him
to the apartment near the University of Chicago where they
were staying.

To make a longer story shorter, we became friends, and before we parted that evening, Julio María had told me, "You
must come to Montevideo. I shall get you an invitation from
the University." He did, with the aid of our own Department
of State, and soon I was really "flying down to Rio."

*   *   *

It had been a rather strange trip. Nancy and I had to travel
in separate planes on different schedules during the day and
had met at night at Port-of-Spain, Trinidad, and at Belem,
Brazil, on the mouth of the Amazon. From there it took me two
days to fly to Rio, with an overnight stay at Pernambuco, while
Nancy, leaving a day later but flying directly across the wild
Brazilian hinterland, had needed only one day for the Belem
to Rio flight. In fact, she landed only twenty minutes after I did.

We had spent a busy and very pleasant week in Rio. I had
visited the laboratory of Professor Carlos Chagas at the National
Medical School one day. On another I had gone out to the
Oswaldo Cruz Institute, where I met the revered H. C. de
Souza Araujo, one of the few world authorities on leprosy. We
had ascended Sugarloaf Mountain on the funicular car for the
unrivaled view of the harbor of Rio, seen the teeming beach at
Copacabana and marvelled at the ultramodern buildings of the
great city.

Best of all, we had finally obtained seats on the same plane
for the remainder of our journey. Now we were flying south
on the last lap of our long voyage. There had been brief stops
at São Paulo and at Porto Alegre but from there it was to be
nonstop to Montevideo. As we descended through the clouds,
we saw for the first time the neat farmland of the Uruguayan
countryside and soon, in the gray distance ahead of us, the city
itself. In a few minutes we had landed at the airport of Montevideo. As the plane door opened, we quickly realized that we
were back in the temperate zone, for it was August, early spring

in this land far below the equator. The skies were dull, and there was a chill breeze blowing.

We had little time to think of the weather. We were being officially welcomed to Uruguay, and it was far more of an event than we ever had anticipated. Newspaper photographers shot us as we descended from the plane, Doctor and Mrs. Sosa rushed forward, *both* to embrace us, and amid the breathless greetings we were presented to the Secretary General of the National University, the Cultural Attaché of the American Embassy and several other personages of note.

"So at last you are really here," Julio María said. "You will find everything prepared for you and Nancy." The four of us entered his car and drove off to the city. But it was not an ordinary drive; rather, it was a whirlwind tour of various parts of the city, with my friend pointing with pride to parks, avenues, and buildings. On this ride and on many another later one, it was clear that driving for Julio María was an incidental occupation which left one hand, and sometimes both hands, free. We reached the central plaza of Montevideo. The scene was a very pleasant one, with graceful palm trees, flower beds and benches. The Presidential Palace and other buildings flanking the plaza were gay with flags, for it was a day of national fiesta.

An enormous edifice reared itself on one side of the open space, a building of curious, almost grotesque, architecture. This was the hotel Palacio Salvo—to be our home for the next four months. I have never known how to describe its architecture, either in modern or in classical terms. It seemed almost as though the builders had been unable to decide whether to top it with domes or towers and had arrived at some sort of compromise between the two. The result, for a twenty-story building, was something resembling the Taj Mahal set on top of a skyscraper. As we exclaimed over this somewhat awesome sight, our friend jested in a fine expansive way, "This," he said, "was built for you—and the flags, they are out for you!"

In the hotel, Sosa was solicitous to see that we were comfortably settled, even to the point of asking, "Do you like one big bed or two little ones?" Our room faced the colorful plaza scene and was provided with its own balcony. For a brief time now we were left alone, but in less than an hour we met in the lobby with representatives of three of the newspapers of Montevideo, with the Cultural Attaché of our embassy, the Secretary-General of the University and Doctor Sosa. Subjects for discussion included international cooperation, the advance of science and the Sosa-Andrew alliance.

✻   ✻   ✻

The next few days were kaleidoscopic, with pictures of long stretches of sandy Uruguayan beach, offices of University executives and faculty, wards and operating rooms, embassy receptions, libraries, luncheons and speeches, and a multitude of new Spanish words and names washing over our minds. Gradually, some of this varied activity began to subside, and the center of our scientific work, the Laboratory for the Investigation of the Biological Sciences, came into sharper focus.

Many of the things which I had seen in these first days in Uruguay presented interesting contrasts between the old and the new—what we were accustomed to thinking of as nineteenth century on the one hand, and what was most modern or ultra-modern on the other. Many of the differences between what we encountered and what we were used to were actually because of the fact that the European influence in Montevideo, particularly the French and Spanish, was as great or greater than was the influence of the States. Not having, at that time, travelled in any countries of Europe, we did not fully realize this.

Of these contrasts between old and new, the building where I worked was an interesting example. Actually, it had been a beautiful residence in the Spanish style. Its conversion to scientific work seemed to be a partial one and one which had not wholly changed the soul of the place. The grounds were surrounded by a high iron fence. Dogs lounged in the driveway just inside, and the formal gardens of the residence had left an abundance of lovely flowering shrubs and herbs around the old building.

The laboratory which Sosa and I, as his guest, occupied was on the ground floor. A laboratory bench ran down the center of the room, and shelves on two of the walls were filled with bottles of chemicals and with books, chiefly in Spanish. For warming slides and solutions, we used not the familiar gas burners of our country, but little alcohol lamps, which, indeed, served quite well.

Our workday was quite different from the type to which I had been accustomed, not particularly easier, but definitely different. I usually would be at the laboratory by 9 A.M., which, in view of the endless events in Montevideo which kept us up into the late evening, was no mean accomplishment. Julio María would come in an hour or so later, but this was by no means the beginning of his day. Medical scientists in Latin America, or at least the great majority of them, find themselves under the necessity of earning an income other than the relatively small salaries which they can earn for purely research or teaching positions. Thus, Doctor Sosa was carrying on a rather active practice to which he devoted his early mornings, late afternoons and some of his evenings. That he was a diligent and conscientious practitioner of medicine, I had no doubt, yet it was easy to see where his true love lay, from his huge enthusiasm for the laboratory and the pursuit of new knowledge.

Many a morning, while I was leaning over a series of staining trays, he would literally bounce through the door, with a loud and cheerful, "Go-od morning, Warren," to which I would return a "Buenos dias." His medical bag stowed in a corner, he would don his long white laboratory coat and take up smoothly the tasks which he had left the previous afternoon.

"Today," he would say, "we must *work.*" The statement was accompanied by a quick, expressive flipping motion of his right hand, a gesture which then and ever since has seemed to me to show most dramatically the impatience of an eager mind with the slow march of events. I have never seen it used by another person! He moved with surprising speed and deftness, carrying tiny sections of nervous tissue through a series of fluids and showing me with pardonable pride the marvellous results which he achieved.

Sosa's methods of working were those, in general, of what we may call the Spanish school of histologists. They are methods the success of which depends upon the individual attention given by the scientific worker to each step and upon his own close familiarity with the details of the work. Histological methods more common in England and in our country have been made more routine and often are carried out, according to direction, by technicians who are not enthusiastically concerned about the results. The great Spanish students of microscopic anatomy were usually their own technicians and developed astonishing methods of bringing out the details of cells and fibers of the body, and especially of the nervous system. Sosa himself had studied under one of the greatest of these, Don Pío del Río Hortega, an exile from Spain who had come to Montevideo and then gone on to Buenos Aires.

Usually an hour or so after his arrival, Julio would very suddenly stop work. "Now, Warren—," he would say, "let us have some coffee," and the laboratory bench would become our kitchen. Often at this time, one or more of the scientists working in other laboratories in the building would join us. One was Carlos Vaz Ferreira, the son of an eminent Uruguayan philosopher and logician. Carlos was a young man of slender build and quiet, serious demeanor. His whole manner was in marked contrast to that of Doctor Sosa, and I often thought on seeing them together how frequently one can go wrong in trying to characterize a Latin American type.

Another visitor at coffee time was Ferreira-Berrutti, a man vaguely reminiscent of Doctor Watson without his Sherlock Holmes, a most pleasant character—*muy simpático* is the best Spanish description—a man for whom one could not help having an instinctive liking. He was a pathologist of no mean ability and had discovered the first case of Chagas' disease, a protozoan infestation, to be found in Uruguay.

During the days in the laboratory, Julio María taught me many things; I learned that what seemed like small tricks of technique are often tremendously important. I learned to carry tissues with me if they required changing from one fluid to another late in the evening or early in the morning. We prepared all of

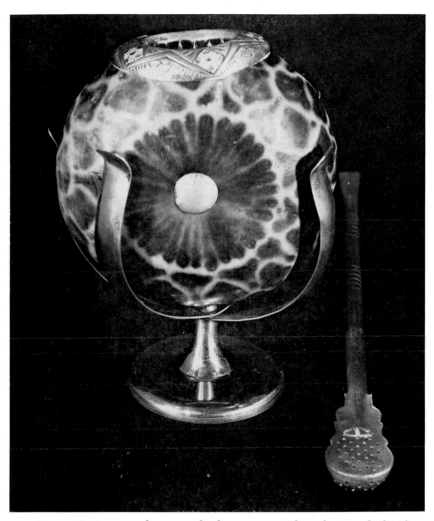

FIGURE 4 Maté, a gourd receptacle for tea as used in the Rio de la Plata region.

our own chemical solutions, weighing out the powder or crystals with great care, measuring the distilled water, the alcohols, formalin, acids and buffers and knowing that the result depended on no one other than ourselves. When I learned more of the ways of working of the great founders of the Spanish school of histology, the primitiveness of some features of our own activities seemed, rather than a handicap, to be a part of the privilege of following in their steps. The master of them all, Santiago Ramón y Cajal, had often worked long hours in an unheated laboratory, wearing an overcoat indoors on the coldest days in Madrid.

We were working on two problems, according to the previous agreement, for one of them had been planned by Doctor Sosa and the other I had suggested. The first dealt with the structure of the roots of the spinal nerves and with the occurrence in them of certain cells not hitherto described. It had full scope for the making of the magnificent silver-impregnated preparations of nervous tissues to which the Spanish techniques are so well adapted. The second problem involved the study of wandering cells, the lymphocytes, which enter into the inner lining layer or epithelium of the intestine. The year before, in my own laboratory, I had found that some of the lymphocytes apparently enter into cells of the epithelial layer. I was eager to confirm this, or to refute it if necessary, with the aid of methods in which Doctor Sosa was particularly proficient, in relation to the demonstration of an internal organ of the cell, the Golgi apparatus. Seen after impregnation studies with metals such as silver and osmium, this is a tiny black net usually near to the nucleus of the cell. About this little structure, which he had studied in many different cell types, including those of such low forms as snails and leeches, Julio María would practically go into raptures. "Thees leetle Golgi apparatus—I love it," he would say, peering through the microscope at some of our more beautiful preparations.

This part of the cell had, for a number of years, been an object of special study by Sosa. At that time, and for some years later, a rather embittered controversy was raging among students of the cell as to whether this netlike structure is really present in the living cell or whether killing the cell and preparing it for study brings about the appearance of the Golgi apparatus— whether it was, in fact, an artifact, something artificially created. In this controversy my friend was an ardent defender of the reality of his beloved Golgi apparatus, but by no means on an emotional basis alone, for long study had made him familiar with the consistent appearance and with the changes under different physiological conditions which it would undergo. In very recent years, new scientific tools, such as the phase microscope for the investigation of living cells and the electron microscope for the probing of "ultramicroscopic" structure, have supported the real nature of the Golgi apparatus and the views of Sosa have been amply vindicated in this regard.

With my friend's love of technical preparation and of the beauties of tissue as brought out in microscopic study, went a great enthusiasm for depicting the objects by means of pen and ink or brush. "I love to draw down," he would say to me. Often he would become completely absorbed in this task, and what had seemed like an hour's work would extend through an entire morning or afternoon as new areas were added to the drawing and greater delicacy and finesse put into its execution.

Ways and attitudes of work were not, however, the only things which I learned during these days at the laboratory. It was always a thrill to come home with a new Spanish phrase or idiom or a wise saying or pungent jest of the Río de la Plata region. One day, Sosa, while working, broke into the strains of a song which seemed to fill the laboratory with delicious, plaintive sound. It was "Adios Muchachos." I expressed my admiration—both for the song and his vocal abilities. "Warren, I shall teach it to you!" he exclaimed, and without further ado the day's work was pleasantly interrupted.

The song goes:

> Adios muchachos, compañeros de mi vida,
> Barra querida, de aquellos tiempos;
> Me toca me hoy emprender la retirada,
> debalejarme d'este muchachada;
> Adios muchachos, ya me voy
> y me resigno,
> Contra el destino, nadie la talla;
> Se acarbaron para mi todas las farras,
> Mi cuerpó enfermo no resiste mas —
> Acuden a mi mente recuerdos de otros tiempos,
> De los bellos mómentos que antaño disfruté;

Cercita de mi madre, santa viejicita,
y de mi noviecita, que tan idolatré,
Recuerd, era hermosa, tan bella que una diosa;
Y que, ebrio con la dicha, le di me corazon!
Mas el Señor, zeloso de sus encantos
Hundiendome en el llanto, me la llevo!
Adios muchachos, etc.

Translated:

Goodbye, boys, comrades of my life,
Beloved old gang of early days,
Now I must retire
And leave this group of boys;
Goodbye, boys, now I go and I resign myself,
No one can win against destiny;
For me all the good times are over,
My sick body no longer resists —
There come to me memories of other times,
Of fine moments that I once enjoyed,
With my mother, sainted old lady,
And my sweetheart, whom I idolized so;
I remember that she was beautiful, lovely as a goddess;
And that, intoxicated with happiness, I gave her my heart!
But the Good Lord, perhaps jealous of her charms,
Cast me into grief, for he took her from me!
Goodbye, boys, etc.

By evening I was brimming over with the song, and as Sosa had filled the laboratory, so I essayed to fill our hotel apartment with melody, how much to the edification of our neighbors I never learned. In any event, it was good for our Spanish!

Some of the English practiced upon me by my *compañeros* was rather amusing. One afternoon, during our break, Ferreira Berrutti asked me, "How many spoons shall I pour in your coffee?"

Nancy and I were frequent guests at the Sosa home. The residential districts of Montevideo are most agreeable places, with broad streets, verdant gardens and houses in varied architecture of cement, tinted in pink, green, blue and other brilliant colors, yet retaining such traditional features as the everpresent balconies. Sosa had his living quarters on the second floor of his home; his medical offices on the first. In his library were many volumes on biology and medicine which I had never seen before or which I may have examined as rather rare items in the States. Here, for instance, were the complete works of Camillo Golgi, the great Italian histologist, and of Ramón y Cajal, the master of Spanish histology (in 1906 these two shared the Nobel prize in medicine for their amazing discoveries on the structure of the nervous system). Here, too, were the collected studies of Retzius, a number of huge tomes, beautifully illustrated with plates from his dissections and microscopic observations.

This was the library of a scholar who went beneath the superficial aspects of his field and who admired with an intense zeal the investigators who had pioneered in it. Sosa told me of his early education and of the constant devotion of his parents, first to his secondary and then to his university training. At seventeen years of age, he was reading Nietsche and was stimulated by the writings of this philosopher with the urge to excel in his undertakings.

Even before entering the University, he and a group of young friends had formed a society with the rather imposing title Instituto de Estudios Cientificos (Institute of Scientific Studies). Seeking guidance, they approached some of the professors at the University. Professor J. A. Collazo, recently returned from Germany, invited Julio María to work in his laboratory on a problem concerning vitamin B and the glycogen of liver and muscle in pigeons. The young Sosa had the honor of presenting a paper on this subject at a scientific meeting in Buenos Aires.

Shortly afterwards, again seeking guidance, Sosa made the acquaintance of Professor Clemente Estable, an Uruguayan who had just returned from two years in Madrid in the laboratory of Ramón y Cajal. Eager to study the cytological basis of the changes in the nervous system in pigeons suffering from a deficiency of vitamin B, Sosa now found a golden opportunity for learning the techniques of microscopic preparation and applying himself to these studies. Professor Collazo was a pure biochemist, but Professor Estable had worked intimately with the master of microscopic technique, and Julio María became his disciple with a huge enthusiasm.

These two professors, Collazo and Estable, had a profound effect on his life and work. Later, Professor R. R. Bensley of the University of Chicago, of whom I have spoken already, was a source of great inspiration.

At his home and in the laboratory, in spite of our rather busy schedule, I was fortunate enough to hear Julio María express on more than one occasion his feelings about scientific investigation. "The urge to seek for truth," he said on one occasion, "For me, this is something inside of me, it is a natural tendency of my spirit. And for me it is the pure science which intrigues—the problems on which I work are not those which give any immediate promise of practical use—oh, yes, some day they may aid medicine, but I study these things because *I want to.*"

Sosa's scientific accomplishments were numerous, but he has felt most satisfaction from two discoveries: (a) the demonstration of a decussation, "a crossing of the ways," of groups of sensory nerve fibers in the lower part of the human brain, and (b) the demonstration of the real existence of the Golgi apparatus by showing it in cells which had not been treated in any manner (this latter was a work carried out some years after my visit to Uruguay and presented before our own American Association of Anatomists in 1953). Both of these studies called for the exquisite powers of technical manipulation and of microscopic observation in which he has excelled.

I have spoken of the physical energy of Julio María. He was a lover of the outdoors and introduced us to one of the most interesting groups to which we ever had been privileged to belong, the Uruguayan society known as Amigos de la Naturaleza, the Friends of Nature.

The first excursion which we made with this group was an exciting experience. We were up and waiting at an ungodly hour. Julio María appeared at our door in sport clothes, with a great knife in his belt. With Isabel and him, we drove to the railroad station where the rest of the group, some twenty-five persons, were waiting. Soon the train was carrying us through the beautiful Uruguayan countryside.

The scenery here was soft and pleasing to the eye and mind,

gently rolling hills, plenty of untrammelled space and well-kept
fields and farmhouses. Among the group were some of the most
likeable and fascinating characters whom we ever had met. The
great poet of Uruguay, Sabat Ercasty, was one of them; Badano-
Repeto, a keen young surgeon and avid naturalist, was another;
and a delightful character named Tschiersky, who had come to
Montevideo from Berlin when Hitler was rising to power, was
a third. Tschiersky enlivened our trip with many tunes on his
harmonica.

We soon alighted at a little station in the country and began
hiking toward our destination, the village of Santa Lucia. Below
the trail on which we were walking were some reed-grown
ponds. The dark patches of water suddenly began to show little
floating islands of vivid pink. In response to our curiosity, some
of the group scrambled down the slope with us, and we soon
were examining for the first time the pink eggmasses of the
great amphibious snail, Ampullaria canaliculata. This is a creature which has both gills and lungs and a sort of long fleshy
tube to reach above the water to receive air if the oxygen dissolved in the water is inadequate. It was not long before we
had several shells of this animal.

Back on the trail, we continued our walk in the warm sun, the
mud soon drying on our boots. Every few minutes, it seemed,
someone along the line would exclaim over the finding of some
object of interest to these roving naturalists. Now it was a bird's
nest, now an ant village and next a lovely patch of wild flowers.

To us it was of much interest that the farming people in
Uruguay do not look on such groups of hikers as trespassers.
The fences which we did come upon were not of barbed wire
and offered no serious obstacle. At noon we ate our lunch in a
grove of pine trees and afterwards continued the ramble. Every
now and then Sabat Ercasty would favor us with the recita-
tion of some verses.

About mid-afternoon we came to the banks of a slow-flowing
river, bordered by willows and with stretches of fairly wide,
sandy beach. Here we met a gaucho with a horse, and some of
the more daring of the group, including Sosa and Tchiersky, put

together to "rent" the horse for short rides on the beach. Sosa rode very well and made a handsome figure astride the proud animal. We contented ourselves with an exploring walk along the banks and skipping flat stones in the calm water. From the river we returned to the station by a different route, and the train took us to Montevideo in time for dinner.

That evening, after dinner, we were invited by an English lady whose acquaintance we had made at the hotel, to come to her balcony on the fifteenth floor. It gave a magnificent view of the broad harbor of Montevideo and the Río de la Plata. The evening sky, deepening from gray to black, was at frequent intervals illuminated by brilliant flashes of lightning. It was an impressive scene, but with a storm on the way we felt glad that we were not still out in the Uruguayan hinterland.

This was only one of a number of expeditions which we made with the Amigos de la Naturaleza. Indeed, we were invited to go with a number of persons from this group up into the jungles of Paraguay, and we would have been tempted to do so, but that the time set was too close to the date of our departure.

Julio María was a man of wide acquaintance and connections, and with my own assignment from the United States Department of State, I was introduced to many persons of note in Uruguay, including the Secretary General of the University, the Minister of Public Health and even the President of the Republic, with whom I had a twenty-minute audience, from which I remember chiefly his own very democratic manner, my words of praise both for Montevideo and the rural areas which we had visited and his speaking of the United States and Uruguay as *paises hermanos*, "brother nations."

During this time, also, I was delivering talks, some in Spanish and some in English, to various scientific and social groups of Montevideo and meeting numerous persons, many from Argentina, some from other countries of Latin America and some from Europe and the United States. Among the visitors from home was Doctor Coolidge of General Electric, a Faraday Medal winner in physics, who had come down for an exposition on "50 Years of X-ray." Among the visitors from Argentina was Francisco Alberto Saez, one of the three authors of the *General Cytology* by De Robertis, Nowinski and Saez, which I later was to translate from Spanish to English.

Spring was well advanced now in the hemisphere below the equator. On clear nights, the Southern Cross blazed in a sky of black velvet over the Río de la Plata. Our trips to the beaches were chiefly within the city, for our time was well filled, but there was an occasional journey to the wilder coast and the little islands where cormorants swam and dived and hosts of strange sea creatures could be found. On these trips Sosa was as enthusiastic a field biologist as he had shown himself as a laboratory scientist.

A few days before one of these expeditions, Julio María told us with some excitement that a formal induction into the Amigos de la Naturaleza was being planned for us. Apparently, we had passed the test of the group in showing a real zest for the natural beauties of Uruguay and of her plant and animal life and also the test of sufficient stamina to keep up on the journeys of exploration!

The ceremony was carried out on a wild beach, the Punta Ballena, with our little group gathered on the sandy floor of a sort of natural amphitheater enclosed on three sides by cliffs some thirty feet high, with great waves breaking upon the rocks on the fourth side. Here we received our "diplomas," and here Sabat Ercasty recited to the group one of his majestic poems *"Alegría del Mar"* ("Joy of the Sea"), the waves raising their voices in accompaniment to that of the great poet. We were presented also with a photograph of the grotto as it appears in its lonesome splendor, and on the margins of the mounting were the signatures of all of the members of the Society. Later, two of the members made us a special gift of one of the books of Sabat Ercasty, *Sinfonía del Río Uruguay,* the frontispiece of which is an excellent photograph of the poet, taken by Doctor Sosa on the shores of a wooded isle. This picture of the rock-and sea-girt amphitheater and this book of verse recall to us vividly the ceremony by the sea.

Our work at the laboratory had gone very well, and in the last week of our stay, Sosa and I completed the writing and illustrations for three joint papers, all of which later appeared in the "Anatomical Record," published by the Wistar Institute Press at Philadelphia.

For our return trip we were to fly to Buenos Aires to spend a few days, then for short visits to: Santiago, Chile; Lima, Peru; Guayaquil, Ecuador; Panama City and so to Miami and home.

On the ninth of January, 1946, Julio María and Isabel came to the airport with us. It had been for us a wonderful four months, and our understanding and affection for our Uruguayan friends had deepened from week to week.

In the years since our visit to "mi amigo," I have many times thought with gratitude of the scientific, intellectual and material benefits which I have derived from his invitation and his hospitality. The lectures, conferences and conversations of those days are still surprisingly fresh in my mind. But I remember most vividly the warmth of Julio María's character, the eager enthusiasm with which he spoke of the "soul" of Uruguay, his little, heart-shaped country and his own vivid zest for life, for work and for friendship.

And, so, when I think of Montevideo and of "mi amigo," the lines of Longfellow ring more truly:

> The heart hath its own memory, like the mind,
> And in it are enshrined
> The precious keepsakes, into which is wrought
> The giver's loving thought.

Chapter 3

THE MAN WHO DISSECTED LENIN'S BRAIN
A Visit to Professor Oskar Vogt

> . . . Alas, poor Yorick! I knew him, Horatio. A
> fellow of infinite jest, of most excellent fancy.

THESE lines from the pensive soliloquy of Hamlet, as he held the skull of a departed friend, seem to us most fitting and appropriate. That whitened reliquary of humanity has a peculiar influence in leading us to reminiscence and to philosophical contemplation.

Like the Pandora's box of ancient legend, this little box of bone has freed a vast host of winged creatures. For from its dark and silent interior have arisen all of the thoughts and plans of mankind. From it have come the mad destructiveness of an Attila and the delicate poetry of a Keats, the consuming fires of the hydrogen bomb and the healing balm of the miracle drugs.

But it is not the box itself, not the whitened skull, which has worked the magic. It is that which lies within—that strange, inscrutable organ, that combination of spirit and matter—the human brain.

It is little wonder that the study of the brain has been a challenge to scientists in many countries and in many times. It has been only within the past century or so, however, that methods have become available to study the microscopic structure and the manner of functioning of its many and complicated parts. In this relatively brief period, a very great deal has been learned, and each new step forward has increased our wonder at the intricacy of design of this master-organ of the body.

31

FIGURE 5   Oskar Vogt.

❊   ❊   ❊

One day there came to my desk an interesting letter—an invitation for me to deliver an address to the Association for Research in Nervous and Mental Disease at the Roosevelt Hotel in New York City. The meeting was some six months later, and preparation of the address, if I accepted, would be a cause for considerable careful study and planning. The letter, from the president of the association, described it as a body "of over 800 distinguished physicians in the fields of neurology and psychiatry." The topic for my presentation was "Structural Changes with Aging in the Nervous System." It was one in which it might seem that I would have considerable knowledge, since I had begun work in that field over twenty years earlier. As a matter of fact, however, while I had contributed a number of papers to the literature, they had all been written and published in that earlier period of my work, and most of my more recent research had not concerned the brain nor other portions of the nervous system. That I had by no means lost interest in this subject, though, was seen in the fact that I recently had resumed some work on the nerve cell, particularly on the minute intracellular elements known as mitochondria. Without a great deal of hesitation, then, I sent an affirmative answer to the invitation by the Association.

It was a few days later, when I had initiated work on the address, that I rather suddenly began to realize that, in spite of my earlier work, I did not feel myself to be quite the authority that I would like to have thought myself or that the honor of the invitation might have indicated me to be. I needed help . . . inspiration . . . information! It is at just such times that a scientific worker may appreciate the value of friendships and close intellectual associations with other scientists. In the present instance, my thoughts turned to my friend, Doctor Webb Haymaker, Chief of the Section of Neuropathology at the Armed Forces Institute of Pathology, and to his wealth of knowledge of the work going on in foreign countries, particularly in Germany. I searched my files and found a reprint of a paper written by Webb in honor of Professor and Madame Oskar Vogt. Yes, this was the professor whom I remembered as having published an article in the English journal "Nature" on the aging of nerve cells. But this reprint told me much more of his eminent accomplishments through a long career of investigations in the anatomy and physiology of the nervous system and in the study of its diseases. The paper, written in 1950, was printed "on the occasion of the 80th birthday of Professor Vogt and the 75th birthday of Madame Vogt."

Here, then, was an eminent foreign scientist to whom I could write and from whom I could learn more of his own work and that of his German colleagues—that is, if 1955 still found him living and active, for by now he would be eighty-five years old!

I sent my "arrow into the air," an epistle to fall to earth at Neustadt in the Black Forest. I had waited but a few days when the reply from Germany reached my desk. It was a warm and helpful answer to my inquiries signed with a firm hand by Professor Vogt himself! But it did not end with written information nor references to the more recent German papers. "The best way for you to learn of our work," said the closing sentence, "is to come over and see for yourself—you will be most welcome!"

The logic of Professor Vogt's reasoning was convincing and the cordiality of his invitation compelling. That same day I resolved on a trip to the Black Forest and a quest for firsthand information on the studies of the great German savant!

❋　❋　❋

As a boy, I sometimes had pictured the Black Forest. It would be a place where the trunks of great trees rose on all sides, shutting out the light of heaven, a somber, forbidding region inhabited by strange forest spirits. My journey from Freiburg to Neustadt showed me that its true aspect was quite different, although no less picturesque. The forest is chiefly one of great, majestic firs, which, straight and tall, climb over the rugged mountainous terrain. There is a regularity and beauty to these armies of trees which was most appealing to me. In early days, the Black Forest was a fine hunting ground for nobility. Even on my short rail trip, I was thrilled at the sight of a graceful fawn leaping up a steep hillside.

Neustadt is in the very midst of this forested country, but the area immediately surrounding the little town was cleared for farming. I alighted from the train and called the Institute, for the exact time of my arrival had not been determined. As the Institute was some little distance from the town proper, a car would come for me. As I stood outside the tiny station, I enjoyed the clear, fresh air of the region. The sun shone brightly, but without undue heat, and the sky was blue and tranquil.

I had not long to wait. A car drove up, and a young German came forward to greet me. "I am Parker," he said. "Professor Vogt has asked me to take you first to your hotel, then to him."

After a few minutes at the little hotel to freshen up, we

drove out from the town and up a winding road. At the forested summit of a hill we stopped. Here was a great iron gate with the forbidding sign *Eintritt Verboten* ("Entrance Forbidden"). Parker alighted to open the gate, and we passed through, continuing between walls of trees. We now were on the grounds of the Institute. Rounding a curve, we came in full sight of the building which served both as laboratory and home for the Vogts. It is a sturdy, efficient-looking building, but softened by flower beds and ornamental shrubs which surround it in profusion. We mounted the stairs and entered a spacious room of the laboratory. The Vogts rose to greet me. Professor Vogt was a powerful-appearing figure, for all of his eighty-five years. His magnificent head was crowned by long white locks and adorned with a full white beard. His aspect was leonine in its strength and bearing. And Madame Vogt bore her eighty years surprisingly lightly.

Professor Vogt wasted no time in approaching the scientific purpose of my visit. As soon as the courteous inquiries concerning the journey were over, he led me into an adjoining room. "When is your address to be?" he inquired. I told him. He picked up a box from the table. "Here," he said, handing me the box, "are the lantern slides for your talk!" I was too surprised at first to give proper thanks. Even so, I did not realize at the time what a rich present he was making to me, for I later found that the box contained thirty-two slides with excellent reproductions from the work of Professor Vogt and his disciples specifically on the subject of my address, changes with age in the nerve cells.

Now things took a somewhat more formal turn. There were other scientific visitors to the Institute, and a lecture by Professor Vogt was scheduled for 10 A.M. As we assembled in the small but well-arranged lecture room, I was introduced to the other visitors.

The Institute for Brain Research at Neustadt, while it perhaps should not be called a Mecca, in the sense of attracting large numbers of pilgrims, is in a true sense a sort of scientific shrine, for students of the nervous system from all parts of the world

make their way here to enjoy the privilege of personal conversations with Professor and Madame Vogt, both of whom are
known in all countries for their contributions to science. There
were some half-dozen visitors. One in particular whom I recall
was Doctor Luis Govi, a neurologist from Buenos Aires. He
was accompanied by his wife and another Argentinian physician.
We talked briefly before the lecture and found that we had a
mutual friend—Doctor Moises Polak of Buenos Aires, the latest
of the disciples of the great Del Río-Hortega, who had been
actively working with the master in Argentina until the latter's
death some years before.

The lecture began. While Professor Vogt had spoken only in
German to me thus far, he delivered his lecture in French. I was
indeed thankful for my earlier studies of this language and for
some weeks in Paris! This first lecture concerned the subject
of my chief interest at the time—aging of the nervous system—
and was richly illustrated with lantern-slides. It was a thrilling
experience to hear this eminent German neurologist describe
changes which in many cases were the same which I myself had
seen in my own laboratory many thousands of miles away across
the sea.

I was back at the hotel for luncheon and enjoyed a brief rest
afterwards, reading in the lobby while awaiting Parker. In a
German periodical, a phrase which amused me was, *"Das Geld
macht nicht fröhlich aber beruhigt die Nerven."* ("Money does
not make a man happy, but it does calm the nerves!").

At the laboratory I now was assigned my own room, where
I could study quietly the slides, reprints and books which the
Vogts made available to me. But best of all, Professor Vogt himself appeared in the early afternoon and sat with me for a
fascinating two and a half hours of personal conversation—a
combination of German, French, and English for both of us;
but we were on common ground, and the occasional effort
to make ourselves understood only added to the intense interest
of this rare opportunity.

I was invited to have dinner with my hosts that evening. By
seven we were gathered in the pleasant dining room on the

FIGURE 6 Oskar Vogt in his Russian cap.

first floor of the Institute, where the living quarters of the Vogts had been established. There were four other guests besides me: a Doctor Rabl from Neustadt (another Neustadt, near Ludwigshafen); a niece of Professor Vogt from Erfurt in the Russian Zone, and two other ladies. There was light conversation and more than one well-placed jest from the Professor. I was much interested in learning more from his niece of her city and of conditions in East Germany, but I was some-what reticent to ask. She spoke of the nearness of Erfurt to Weimar, so well known as the home of Goethe and for other classical associations, and also in the Russian Zone. She spoke also of their tomato garden, for they lived on the outskirts of Erfurt. She was on holiday and apparently travelled fairly freely between East and West.

We moved into the living room for our coffee and after-dinner conversation. It was a spacious room with large glass-faced bookcases along two of its walls. I was curious as to the nature of the books which our host would have in his general library. The variety of titles was very great indeed. Among others, there was a large volume on *The Flora of Guernsey Island,* and a large number of the red-backed Baedeker guides of various countries were conspicuous. Conserving his energy, Professor Vogt relaxed on a comfortable lounge during our cof-fee, but he rose to bid us good evening as Doctor Rabl and I were leaving for the town.

It was a fine night, and we walked from the Institute through the private forest, out of the great iron gate and down the winding road to the town. On the way, Doctor Rabl told me something of his own work in pathology, of the coming meet-ing (1956) of the Deutsche Anatomische Gesellschaft in Stock-holm and of the fact that there are in Germany twenty-four towns named Neustadt! I slept well that night with a heavy blanket over me, a rather odd protection for a North Carolinian in early August.

The days of that short week with Professor Vogt are mem-orable ones. Each morning began, after breakfast, with the walk in the fine mountain air up to the Institute, where I would ar-rive a little after eight. Part of each morning was spent in private study of slides with the excellent Zeiss microscope which was furnished to me. Each morning also, however, a formal lecture was given by Professor Vogt to the other visitors and myself.

The excellent projection of lantern slides was a feature of these lectures. A Zeiss model projector, a type which I never before had seen, was used. Here the lantern slides simply were laid flat on a plate of glass.

In my private studies, I enjoyed the privilege of approaching Professor Vogt at almost any time with questions concerning the sections of brain which were given me. In turn, he would call me in to see a particularly fine microscopic field. I recall particularly two such fields—one was of a giant cell—a cell of Betz in a senile brain. It was the most beautiful view of such a cell that I ever had seen. The other was a cell from the globus pallidus of a one-hundred-year-old man. This cell, from the region controlling motor activity, was loaded with the bright yellow-green old-age pigment.

The collection of human brain material which Professor Vogt has made represents a tremendous amount of work and an amazing personal accomplishment. There are some 25,000 sections per brain and over 500 brains! Many of the brains are those of eminent persons with special talents: Krebs of Berlin, who spoke sixty languages fluently; Ysaye, the great Belgian violinist and Ostwald, the eminent physicochemist.

In the hallway was a fine portrait of the Swedish neurologist, Henschen. One evening at dinner, I rather innocently asked Professor Vogt, "Did you know Professor Henschen well?" "Oh yes, indeed," replied my host. "You know, we have his brain."

Both Professor and Madame Vogt had visited in Russia before the Revolution in 1917. They also had returned after the Civil War, and so they had seen the Russian people in these critical times. Madame Vogt, in particular, told me of her regard for them and their intelligence, at the same time deploring the dictatorial nature of the Stalinist regime which had lasted for so many years. At the death of Lenin in 1924, the Russians turned to Professor and Madame Vogt to aid in the immortalization of their great hero of the Revolution by making a careful study of that physical instrument of his mind and spirit—his brain. One afternoon in the laboratory, they told me something of this unique experience. Madame Vogt spoke of how the brain was taken out of a great glass jar by the Russians and handed to her for the gross studies. She made most careful drawings of it from various aspects. The Vogts had the sectioning done under their close supervision. There were 34,000 individual sections prepared and stained.

What did the brain of Lenin reveal? Of course, not even the most involved of anatomical studies can tell us the value of a man's life, can say whether he was right or wrong in his thinking and in his decisions. Lenin's early struggles, the execution of his older brother as an enemy of the Tsar, his exile to Siberia and his labors in the Russian underground could not be revealed by the microscope. Among the things that the Vogts did feel could be seen was a high degree of development of those layers and areas of the cerebral cortex involved in associative thinking —a conclusion which, after all, was not too surprising.

The day for my departure from Neustadt arrived all too soon. "You must come again," Professor Vogt told me. "And next time, I shall show you my collection of bees." The study of the varieties of bees and particularly of the color sequences among them is a field in which the professor was perhaps as famous as in the study of the human brain.

From Neustadt I travelled back by train to Freiburg, then to the Swiss frontier city of Basel and from there by swift express to Paris. During the trip I reread, with new appreciation, the paper which my friend, Doctor Webb Haymaker, had written five years before in homage to the Vogts. The story of their lives and associations reads almost like a history of the progress of knowledge of the nervous system in Europe in the late nineteenth and early twentieth centuries. Both well trained in medicine and in scientific investigation, their own contributions are contained in over 150 papers.

In 1931, a great new brain institute, the Kaiser Wilhelm Institute for Brain Research, had been opened for them in Buch, a suburb of northern Berlin. The rise of Hitler found them out of sympathy with the government. Professor Vogt was, at least, permitted to name his successor at Berlin and to carry with him to his retreat in the Black Forest the most remarkable collection of brains which the world has ever known.

Chapter 4

HE CONQUERED THE INVISIBLE DRAGONS

A Visit to Sir Alexander Fleming

ONCE UPON a time, the fair countries of mankind were being invaded by invisible dragons. The terrible creatures came flying through the air, swimming through the waters and rising from the very soil. Men, women and children were suffering and dying by thousands. The weapons which men had for fighting these tiny dragons were not strong nor powerful enough to save the unhappy victims.

Then a great and good man, who had seen much of the suffering, sought a new weapon—and found it. From the delicate threads of a strange living thing he obtained a golden potion, and with it he struck again and again against the dragons. Many human beings who would have died grew well and strong. Everywhere the horrid invaders were forced to fall back.

For his conquest of the invisible dragons the great man was knighted by the king of his own country and received many honors from the grateful people of other countries all over the world . . .

Thus might a teller of tales describe the work of Sir Alexander Fleming, the discoverer of penicillin.

❊ ❊ ❊

It was not raining that morning when I opened my eyes. Ordinarily, such a statement hardly would be necessary, but in London, in the summer of 1954, this statement meant unusual weather. I had a slight sense of disorientation, of not knowing exactly where I was or why. Most of us, I believe, feel this way occasionally when awakening in a place far off from home

FIGURE 7 Sir Alexander Fleming.

and especially after many new experiences have filled our
minds with varied impressions.

It was Monday after the week of the International Congress
of Gerontology which Nancy and I had been attending. We
were staying in modest, but pleasant, quarters on quiet Half
Moon Street, just a block off from busy Piccadilly. The meetings
had been full of interest for both of us, with numerous scientific
papers and with a series of really brilliant receptions. Our evenings had been spent in succession at Lancaster Palace, the
residence of the Lord Mayor of London, the Royal College of
Physicians, Covent Garden (the Royal Opera House) and the
House of Lords. These social events had given the delegates,

coming from many countries, an opportunity to mingle and talk informally in settings rich in the traditions and history of England.

I allowed the scenes of the past week to come and go in a kaleidoscopic manner in the interior of my mind for some moments. Then my volition took over and drew into sharper focus the present and the immediate future. Yes, this was the morning on which I was to visit Sir Alexander Fleming! Everyone in civilized countries today knows the name "penicillin", but how many have been privileged to talk with the discoverer of this marvellous product face to face? Yet here was I with an invitation not only to spend some time with him, but to do so in the very laboratory in which, years before, the great discovery had been made.

There was a stirring in the next room. Nancy was up, and our breakfast was being brought in to us in our chambers, a convenience which our landlord had insisted on arranging for us. I swung out of bed, washed and dressed, and we soon were enjoying our bacon and eggs and hot tea. (One of the first mornings in London, the little maid, trying to be kind to the Americans, had brought us "coffee"—English variety. Since then we had specified tea!)

There was a little discussion between us, as we finished breakfast, as to whether or not I should wear a trenchcoat on my trip. Nancy urged me either to wear or carry it, but I, rejoicing at the fact that it was not raining a drop, and always liking to feel free and untrammelled, decided this time to go without, in spite of the gray and rather forbidding skies.

I said goodbye, walked down the two steep flights of stairs, out to Half Moon Street, and over to the underground station on Piccadilly. As the swift escalator carried me down to the lower level, I was thinking of what I might encounter that morning. What type of laboratory would this great man have for his work? How would I, a scientist and medical man, but in quite a different field of work, be received? Would he, as he well might, turn me over to an assistant to see the laboratory? Would

I, in fact, actually have an opportunity to spend any time with the renowned microbiologist?

I boarded a westbound train and sped out to Earl's Court. Here I was to transfer to a second train. I came up the stairs to a huge covered station at ground level. It was dry here on the platform, but just beyond, to my dismay, I saw a driving sheet of rain. My optimism had been unfounded! There was nothing for it now, however, but to go on and to hope that I would not have to walk too far from my last train stop to the laboratory. The next train carried me to the Paddington Station underground stop, and I came up to the street just across from that great railroad station. It was still raining—and hard. I waited for the light, then ran across the street and took what scant cover I could as I started off, hugging the buildings. I knew the general direction, but I wanted to get more specific directions and to find out how far I had to go. I stepped into the lobby of a small hotel, obtained the information that I wanted and let some of the water drip off. It was still about two blocks.

The laboratory of Sir Alexander Fleming was in the building now known as the Wright-Fleming Institute, which is connected with St. Mary's Hospital Medical School. The district, while far from the central part of London, is a busy commercial one. The streets were crowded as I started out again. About midway, I stopped at a little restaurant and sat down to a steaming cup of tea. This national drink certainly goes well with the spells of bad weather in England. It offers both a physical counter-actant to the damp and cold and a mental and spiritual comfort to the person who has been caught in it, as I was that day. I walked on, reinvigorated. I entered the hall of the Institute, and a porter led me up the stairs to the second floor. We stopped at a door on which the name "Sir Alexander Fleming" was written. I was ushered in.

The room was a small one—not nearly as large as my own office in the States. It was about twelve feet wide by twenty long. It seemed to be part office and part laboratory. On one end of a long bench running beside the windows was a type-writer and a partly full cup of tea. A very personable young lady rose from a chair and greeted me. "Please be seated. I'll tell Professor Fleming that you are here," she said. I was left alone.

Now I had time to observe my surroundings more closely. I began to note certain features of the room that were to me most unexpected. On the wall at the far end were several large framed pictures. One was of Bill Boyd! Another was of Marlene Dietrich! They bore greetings of these famous stars to the great scientist. Another frame enclosed a certificate of the grant of the Medal of Honor, bestowed by the Canadian Pharmaceutical Manufacturers.

On the wall nearer to me was a framed copy of a poem, from the *Child's Guide to Science*. It carried above a humorous caricature of Albert Einstein and below one of Sir Alexander Fleming, with a little verse about each.

The furnishings were simple. There was an ancient desk with many small pull-out drawers, a table, two metal file cabinets, two metal clothes closets and a tall cabinet or bookcase of antique type.

Now the door opened—but it was not Sir Alexander. It was a lovely young woman in a white laboratory coat—Lady Alexander Fleming—the second wife of the great bacteriologist. They were married in 1953. She is a Grecian beauty from Athens, who is a bacteriologist of note in her own right.

Lady Fleming told me that her husband was at a meeting in the Institute which would be ending at any moment and that he would be along directly. We chatted a little about the weather and the Institute, and she excused herself to look after a batch of medium which she had been "cooking" for some fortunate bacteria.

Lady Fleming had been gone only a few moments when the door opened and Sir Alexander entered. I had seen him before, but usually at a distance or in the company of many other persons. He was a striking figure of a man, although not in the sense in which that description usually is employed. He was not tall, but was well and squarely built, with broad shoulders and an aspect of great solidity. His face was magnificent—a broad

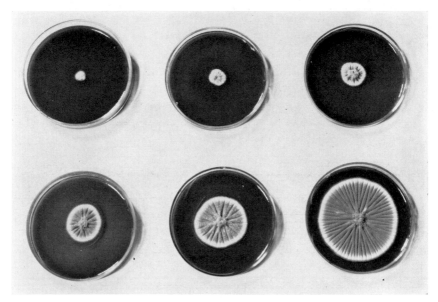

FIGURE 8   Cultures of Penicillium notatum, Fleming's original strain, in progressive stages of development. (Reproduced by kind permission of N. N. Collins, Publishers, London.)

forehead, strong lines of mouth and jaw and penetrating eyes which seemed to be seeing more than is visible to ordinary men. His hair was silvery white, but amply thick. His whole appearance was that of a man much younger than the seventy-three years which the calendar gave him.

He greeted me cordially. His speech had a rich Scottish accent. His boyhood days were spent on a farm in remote Ayrshire, and he attended Kilmarnock Academy in Scotland. We both smiled over my optimism that morning concerning the London weather. At least, I was pretty well dried out by this time, although I am afraid my suit still hung rather limply on me.

I inquired whether Sir Alexander had been long in these quarters. "Yes," he told me. "In fact, this is the laboratory in which the effects of penicillin on bacteria first came to my notice. My present workroom, though, is next door."

"Would you," I asked, "be willing to tell me in your own words how you made the great discovery?"

"Why, yes, of course, if you wish," he replied. "But wait—
I can show you how it happened—." He turned and went over
to the antique cabinet in one corner, slid open a glass door,
reached in and brought out a flat glass dish about three inches
wide and less than half an inch thick, with a snugly fitting glass
cover. I recognized it as a petri dish, a common type of con-
tainer on which bacteria are grown in laboratories. The scientist preparing such cultures pours a warm liquid medium con-
taing agar, a jellylike product of the seaweed, nutrient peptones
from proteins, meat extract and a little salt, all dissolved in
water, into the dish. As it cools, it forms a smooth solid layer on
the bottom. Such a medium offers a fine "soil" for bacteria, and
also for molds. In fact, if one but lifts the lid of such a dish for
a moment in the supposedly clean air of a classroom or laboratory and examines it again the next day after incubation, he
will find numerous round colonies of bacteria, each consisting of
millions of individuals. These colonies are grown from single
bacteria which settled on the agar in that brief space of time.

Fleming brought the dish over to me. "Here is the original
plate," he said, "on which observations of the antibiotic action
of the mold, Penicillium, first were made. That was in 1928."

I leaned forward, intensely interested. I had no idea that this
plate still was in existence. The surface of the agar showed a
number of the familiar round colonies of bacteria. But in one
corner was a different type of colony—a relatively large mass
of mold, a tangle of thousands of delicate threads. This was a
particular species of the genus Penicillium, to which many of
the richly blue-green molds which we see on old orange or
lemon peels belong. It is the millions of tiny reproductive structures, or spores, which give the color. The main mass of this
fungus consists of transparent, branching threads, the mycelium.

"I preserved the colonies by pouring formalin over them,"
said Sir Alexander. "But see, here—," he pointed to an area just
around the mold growth. It was free of bacterial colonies! "So
far, and no farther!" the Penicillium had seemed to say. "It was
this phenomenon," he continued, "that made me feel it probable
that the Penicillium mold forms some type of substance which

prevents the growth of bacteria. "But," and he smiled, "I was not happy when I first saw the mold—it was a contaminant on this plate!"

A contaminant is an organism which has gained access to the medium by accident. The bacterial colonies, Fleming now told me, were meant to be alone on the plate and to represent pure cultures of Staphylococcus organisms—tiny spherical bacteria which grow in clusters like grapes. So it really was an accident, this first clear demonstration of the antibacterial action of Penicillium!

To the mind of a great scientist like Sir Alexander Fleming, however, no phenomena of nature are too insignificant or accidental to be unworthy of notice. Such minds are on the alert, ever aware that nature may be trying to communicate, as it were, some of her great truths through seemingly unimportant details, if only we are ready to receive and interpret them. So it was with the discovery of penicillin. For many years Fleming had sought for a substance which would kill bacteria without adversely affecting the defensive powers of the body, such as our white blood cells, whose task it is to destroy invading organisms. The First World War had taken him away from St. Mary's Hospital to serve as a captain in the Royal Army Medical Corps. In France he had seen how ineffective were many of the older antiseptics used to treat wounds—not only inefficient against bacteria, but harmful to the human tissues. Since then he had been a determined seeker for a better weapon against bacteria.

Here, then, was a ray of hope—a possible weapon for development. Here also was something of immediate usefulness in the studies which Doctor Fleming was making. "At that time," he said, "I was working on the problems of influenza, and it was highly important for me to be able to raise pure colonies of the 'bacillus of influenza.' I had experienced considerable trouble with the staphylococci as contaminants in my cultures. Perhaps this mold, or a product of it, might be used to prevent such contaminants from growing. I tried it. Sure enough, the staphylococci were kept from growing, while my 'influenza organisms' flourished. The product of the mold seemed actually to dissolve the colonies of cocci. It was what we term 'bacteriolytic.' You see, I had every reason for going on with the studies on Penicillium!"

Fleming did go on, but it was not by any means an easy task to obtain the active antibacterial substance from the mold. He found various ways to grow the Penicillium and test its action. He showed by experiments on white mice that it did not injure the white blood cells of the body.

Fleming's first study on Penicillium was published soon after the discovery, in 1929. "It was only years later, though," he told me, "that it became possible to produce really effective penicillin as a drug." For this phase of the work, Sir Alexander gave very ample credit to the Oxford University pathologist, Howard Walter Florey, who, together with Ernst B. Chain and Mrs. Florey, set out in a determined effort to produce a drug from the mold.

From the shining golden droplets which the mold formed when growing in broth in test tubes, a yellowish powder was obtained—penicillin. Soon this powder was proved effective in saving the lives of animals injected with enormous numbers of deadly germs. Next came the supreme test—the early work with human beings! It was tried first only on the most serious, even hopeless cases, so that not all of those treated survived their infections. But soon the record began to show an astounding number of rapid and complete recoveries from the worst types of infection.

Doctor Fleming, like many really great scientists, was cautious in his conclusions and conservative in his statements. Still, as the records grew in number and in impressiveness, he himself said, "People have called it a miracle. For once in my life as a scientist, I agree. It *is* a miracle and it will save thousands of lives."

In 1945, the Nobel prize for medicine was awarded to Fleming, Florey and Chain.

It was a revelation to me to see how fresh was Sir Alexander's manner of recounting the story of his great discovery and with what care, even reverence, he handled the original culture plate, now over twenty-five years old. When happenings are important and interesting enough, the passage of years cannot dim the memory of them.

"Do you," I asked Sir Alexander, "by any fortunate chance still have a reprint of your original article?" I really expected a negative answer, as reprints or separates of important articles often are in great demand soon after the article has been published in a scientific journal.

"Yes, I do," Sir Alexander replied. "And I shall be happy to give you one." He returned to the cabinet and took out a pamphlet which he handed to me with a smile. It is a twelve-page paper entitled, "On the antibacterial action of cultures of a Penicillium, with special reference to their use in the isolation of B. influenzae." It was published in the *"British Journal of Experimental Pathology,"* volume X, in 1929. It is written in scientific language, of course, but with a simplicity and straightforwardness characteristic of the author.

Two of the ten conclusions on the last page of the little, uncovered pamphlet, struck my eye as I turned it over:

> 7. Penicillin is non-toxic to animals in enormous doses and is non-irritant. It does not interfere with leucocytic (white blood cell) function to a greater degree than does ordinary broth.
>
> 8. It is suggested that it may be an efficient antiseptic for application to, or injection into, areas infected with penicillin-sensitive microbes.

How prophetic was this last sentence!

I took my leave of Sir Alexander with a deep sense of the privilege which I had enjoyed in this visit and with an indelible impression of the man and of the scientist imprinted on my mind.

❊ ❊ ❊

Outside it was still raining. I made my way back to the Paddington Station and took a train bound for the center of London. I was on my way to the Arts Club on Dover Street. I had received an entré to this club through a letter of introduction from the Cosmos Club, where I have spent so many pleasant hours in Washington.

As I passed the ancient porter's chair in the hall, the doorman greeted me cordially. I went into the dining room and sat down at a long table where about a dozen men already were having lunch. I ordered mine.

I have not found the aloofness of the British, which is emphasized in some of our literature, to be a very constant trait. A few minutes after I had arrived, the gentleman next to me, as typically British as one could wish in other respects, opened a conversation with me. I soon had learned that he is an artist of some note and he, in turn, had learned my reasons for being in England.

As we talked along, it occurred to me that the visit to Sir Alexander which I had just made would be of interest to my new friend, and I described it briefly.

"As a matter of fact," my friend remarked, "we are awfully proud of Sir Alexander. I happen to have had the pleasure of seeing a fair amount of him socially—."

He paused, smiling, as from an amusing thought. Then he exclaimed, "Bit of luck, though, wasn't it?—that piece of fluff flying in there!"

It was a wonderful example of British understatement, but I could agree with him! A bit of luck—not only for Sir Alexander Fleming—but for countless millions of human beings all over the world who otherwise would fall victims to the ravages of the invisible dragons!

Chapter 5

OF RATS AND MEN—AND ETERNAL YOUTH
A Visit to Vladimir Korenchevsky

> The days of our years are threescore years and ten; and if by reason of strength they be fourscore years, yet is their strength labor and sorrow; for it is soon cut off, and we fly away.

TO OUR human mind, the vastness of time overwhelms even more than the vastness of space. All of the events of history have occurred in a period of insignificant duration when compared to the age of our earth—and for how many billions of years before our earth existed did the myriad stars and galaxies shine in the heavens? The future—it is an endless black tunnel of time—we can imagine no end. Yet the psalmist spoke truth in allotting to us only a brief span of years—nor has this span altered appreciably since his time. Yes, it is true that the *average* life span is far greater than a few generations ago, but this is due chiefly to the conquest of many of the diseases of childhood and youth. The creeping debilities of age are as inimical as ever, nor is their advance retarded to any great extent. Perhaps the Rabbi Ben Ezra spoke well when he bade us:

> Grow old along with me!
> The best is yet to be,
> The last of life, for which the first was made.

Yet too often to the vigorous mind and the great soul the shadows begin to lengthen when it seems that the day's work only has begun. Too often, the rich fruits of experience and the wisdom of age are lost to mankind, when the degeneration of age carries the teeming mind into the obscurity of invalidism or death.

FIGURE 9   Vladimir Korenchevsky.

No wonder, then, that some of our great men of science have asked themselves "Must this thing be? Is it inevitable that the aged become enfeebled? Is the time of final surrender to death set for us in the laws of the universe? Or—brave thought—or blasphemous? should man here also, as in so many other of his efforts—attempt to rise above the limitations imposed by nature?"

In recent years, the scientist has answered this question, at least in part. The mysteries of aging have become a real and accepted field of scientific study. In many laboratories, both government and private, and in many countries of the world, investigators are delving into the differences between young and old animals; mice; rats; guinea pigs; yes, and human beings, where such studies can be done without harm to the subjects. What the results will be eventually in terms of the extension of man's life beyond the "threescore years and ten" and whether the fourscore (or more) must mean "labor and sorrow" remains for the future to tell. Certain it is that the study of the aging process, *Gerontology*, has become an accepted realm of scientific endeavor, that the facts and concepts arising from these new studies have been enough to fill a number of bulky volumes in several languages and to keep in publication journals of reports on the latest studies, each issue of which is awaited eagerly by the explorers of this new realm.

Already much has been learned about the nature of the conditions which steal upon the body in old age and rob it of its strength and well being. Already medical men are putting into practice the knowledge acquired in the laboratory. How far will the advances go? What will old age be like some hundreds or thousands of years from now? We cannot predict with any assurance of accuracy, but we can be sure that much will be done. And as we watch our present progress in these areas on the frontiers of knowledge, we must think with deep gratitude of the pioneers who have devoted themselves to the breaking down of prejudice against such studies and who have laid for all mankind a solid scientific foundation on which to build this new knowledge of the aging process.

＊　＊　＊

I had for many years known of the name and something of the work of Vladimir Korenchevsky. My own deep interest in the study of the aging process had made such a knowledge inevitable—for to think of studies in this field in Europe was to think of Doctor Korenchevsky.

The interest attaching to our visit that day was heightened by the fact that the laboratory of Doctor Korenchevsky was at Oxford, a name so revered by all lovers of higher learning and of English history.

The county town of Oxford, seat of the ancient University, is only a little over sixty miles northwest of London. Here, hundreds of years before our great Harvard and Yale had their beginnings, Oxford University already was rich in tradition. Its origin goes back at least to the first half of the twelfth century, and by 1265 it was spoken of as second only to Paris in its academic renown. Roger Bacon, John Wycliffe and John Duns Scotus added luster to this center of learning of the Middle Ages.

We left London from the Paddington Station and soon were rolling along at a great rate through the pleasant green English countryside. In our compartment was one other person, a dignified man carrving a bookbag. This was our first visit to Oxford, but we did not see it at first as the home of the renowned University, but rather as a busy industrial town with smoke pouring from many smokestacks—symbols of the British motor industry. We knew that Doctor Korenchevsky's laboratory was in the department of physiology near to the University Museum and that he would be expecting us. From the railroad station we went by taxi to the laboratory.

Doctor Korenchevsky himself met us at the door. He was a man of seventy-odd, but with an amazingly erect carriage and a firmness of physique which paralleled his firmness of mind and purpose. His white hair was combed back close to his head, and his keen eyes twinkled behind his glasses. His eyebrows were black and formed a striking contrast to the whiteness of his hair. The skin of his face, except for a few "lines of thought" on his forehead, was remarkably smooth. He was a man of undeniable dignity and also of undeniable charm.

He greeted us with warm enthusiasm, and we soon were deep in the subject of his greatest interest—the mysterious process of aging. Doctor Korenchevsky kept his animals (pedigreed rats) close to his place of work; they were cared for by his assistants most meticulously, and the cages were not only cleaned frequently, but also sterilized with Lysol®. Our host was at pains to show us how well-protected from drafts were his experimental animals. His assistant seemed to be a most able and conscientious young lady. He was of the opinion that no effort was too great to control the conditions under which animals used for such studies are kept. "You see," he said, "many experimenters pay little attention even to the more common infections." He held up his hand and explained proudly, "We, on the other hand, inoculate our rats against their enemies, the paratyphoid bacilli, as carefully as human beings are inoculated against typhoid fever. Why not?"

And indeed it was a good question. Certainly this man had a wonderful background for awareness of the world of micro-organisms and their effects on the bodies of experimental animals and of man. His very first published work, carried out at the Imperial Medical Academy in Petrograd, had dealt with the effects of poisons on single-celled organisms, and for it he had received a gold medal from the Academy.

In Petrograd (St. Petersburg) he had carried out the first portion of his medical studies, graduating there with distinction in 1903. We could picture the young Korenchevsky as a medical student in this great City of the Tsars. Here was a capital built almost within the Arctic Circle, a creation of the mind of one man, Peter the Great. It was to be his "window to the west," for it lies upon the Gulf of Finland at the mouth of the mighty Neva. The almost insuperable task of creating here a cultured metropolis was carried out by autocratic command, first by laborers from every race in the great empire and then by settlers who were commanded to become its citizens—not only the poor, but many among the rich and powerful of his subjects.

At the beginning of this century, when the young Korenchevsky paced its streets, St. Petersburg was a city of churches and monuments, of palaces and bridges, wide avenues and squares—a city which at that time was described by some visitors as "too big for its population"; yet it must have been an impressive and inspiring city, though for many months of the year its vast squares and broad streets were wrapped in swirling snow, its waters hidden beneath thick layers of ice, and its inhabitants, in their great coats and fur hats, passed like phantoms along its enshrouded ways.

This was the capital where the Tsar Nicholas II and his family dwelt in the huge winter palace, not dreaming that a greater storm than any Russian winter was to engulf them before many years had passed.

His studies at Moscow University brought him his M.D. degree and a Privat-Docent Lectureship there. During this period of his education he journeyed to Paris to work in the Pasteur Institute. This was the institute founded in 1888 as a result of Pasteur's remarkable success in producing a vaccine against the deadly hydrophobia. Here thousands of persons had received the Pasteur treatment to prevent the onset of this disease. The Pasteur Institute, however, had now grown, and its research interests were much expanded. Yet the beneficent and inspiring presence of Louis Pasteur, who had passed on in 1895, remained in its laboratories, and the young scientists there could be inspired by viewing daily the very test tubes and retorts which had been Pasteur's own tools, the academic robes which he had worn on ceremonial occasions and the prizes which a greatful France had bestowed upon him. At the Institute, Korenchevsky carried on research under Professor Elie Metchnikoff. Metchnikoff himself is a mighty figure in the history of biological and medical science. While studying minute sea organisms, with their transparent bodies, he saw living cells devouring particles, "phagocytizing" them. It was he who showed that much of the process of defense against bacteria carried out by our own bodies is, by this same process, carried out in our tissues by the white cells of the blood, the leucocytes. It was Elie Metchnikoff, also, who, fascinated by the problems of life and death and aging, theorized on the causes of what he felt to be a premature aging in mankind. In a famous work, *The Prolongation of Life, Optimistic Studies*, he put forward the idea that autointoxication, caused by absorption of products of decay through the walls of the large intestine, had much to do with the decline of the vital processes. This, then, was the stimulating personality who helped to guide the eager-minded Korenchevsky in Paris.

Returning to Russia and completing his medical studies, he became associated with another renowned scientist, Professor I. P. Pavlov, whose name is so intimately associated with ringing bells, hungry dogs and conditioned reflexes.

Before the time of the Bolshevik Revolution of 1917, Korenchevsky held the professorship of experimental pathology at the

Imperial Military Medical Academy, as well as a professorship
in the Second Petrograd University.

He was condemned to liquidation by the revolutionary government, but fled to the south of Russia and thence emigrated
to England in 1920. Here he became a research worker for the
Lister Institute of Preventive Medicine and for twenty-five
years labored in this post. It was in 1945 that a long-cherished
ambition was fulfilled—the ambition to concentrate his efforts
upon the problems of the mysterious processes of aging! In
this year, the British Society for Research on Ageing appointed
him to organize and direct the Gerontological Research Unit at
Oxford. Financial assistance was furnished by Lord Nuffield,
and the work was begun.

FIGURE 10   Coat of Arms of Oxford University.

This, then, was the man who now was telling us so enthusiastically of the carefully controlled conditions of life under which
his experimental animals lived and grew old. He described in
some detail the investigations on the role of the ductless glands
in aging: the thyroid gland, controller of the rate of chemical
changes in the body; the adrenal gland, regulator of fluid balance and guardian of the body in all emergency or stress situa-
tions, the special endocrine parts of the sex glands, and the

pituitary, the great master gland which lies deep within the skull and rules the actions of all of the others.

Dr. Korenchevsky now suggested lunch and the four of us walked over to the famous George's restaurant. Here our host had reserved places and had even arranged for our menu. The British were still under a strict rationing system at this time (1949), and we were amazed to be served a not easily obtained delicacy—chicken!

During lunch we learned more of the history of our host and found that it carried tense drama as well as scientific importance. After the great revolution, Korenchevsky, a man of democratic mind, soon found himself in dispute with the new communist authorities, for he could not refrain from a defense of true freedom in the Academy and in the universities. Things went from bad to worse, and one day he received a warning from a friend that he was to be arrested and shot. To make matters still worse, he was at the time in bed with influenza and a high fever. He could not walk, let alone attempt flight!

The next day a detachment of soldiers arrived. Meanwhile, a bold plan had evolved in Doctor Korenchevsky's mind. "Be careful," the courageous doctor told them. "I am suffering from typhus". Indeed, at that time a serious epidemic of this contagious disease was raging in Russia, and the soldiers were by no means anxious to expose themselves further. "We shall return in three days," said the officer and led his men away. On the second day, Korenchevsky's temperature fell and, weak and ill though he still was, he fled the city and made his way to South Russia. There he served for some time with the White Army as a physician, and when it was defeated made his way via Belgrade and Paris to England.

All of this seemed a long way from the pleasant surroundings of the restaurant. Korenchevsky talked to us now of his long and intense interest in the problems of aging. It was in 1907 that he became, as he himself put it, "suddenly and unexpectedly" interested in gerontology. It was during a visit to a Moscow infirmary for old people. "I was appalled," he said, "by the obviously premature and abnormal senility of the inmates, many of whom had sunk to the animal level and were dying slowly in the worst conditions of physical and mental decay." When he compared what he saw here with some of the vigorous older men and women whom he knew, in whom a love of life and of work burned strongly, he felt the great need for more knowledge of the aging process.

Our lunch hour had been a long one. Doctor Korenchevsky had now to return to the laboratory, but he asked his assistant to guide us to some of the colleges and other places of interest. Somewhat apologetically he said, "As for myself, I scarcely know one college from another. I am thinking always of my rats!"

We were taken first to the venerable Bodleian Library. The moment that we left the comparative brightness of the outside, we were struck by the stillness and solemnity of the place. The ponderous shelves with volume upon volume of learned lore, the windows of painted glass and the quiet, scholarly attitude of the readers impressed us even more than the information that over 700,000 books and some 30,000 manuscript volumes are housed here. Then we visited Balliol College, one of the most ancient, founded in 1263. Magdalen College was next in our tour, and finally Christ Church, founded by Cardinal Wolsey. In the last-named college we were particularly impressed by the great old kitchen, with cooking arrangements not too different from what they must have been centuries before.

In the Great Hall were portraits of many of the eminent men who had studied and worked at Christ Church. Two whom we well remember are John Wesley, founder of Methodism, and Charles Lutwidge Dodgson, the quiet mathematician who wrote and published his charming fantasies under the name of "Lewis Carroll".

No one from the United States who walks among the colleges of Oxford can fail to be somewhat surprised at the *real* antiquity of the buildings and also the *real* lack of repair, externally at least, in which some are seen. The great blocks which form the walls of the ancient buildings in many cases are literally crumbling away, with large jagged interruptions of their continuity.

We returned to the laboratory by a different route, and then all repaired to tea at a small restaurant. Over the teacups, Korenchevsky talked with fervor of the need for strengthening the national societies for the study of aging and of building a strong international association for the interchange of scientific concepts and plans. Although he did not stress the point, it was clear that he himself had sacrificed much in his efforts in this direction and at times had risked not only his reputation but even his position and livelihood.

A very large part of the work of Korenchevsky has shown a selfless devotion to the organization of societies and committees in the field of gerontology. He was instrumental in the setting up of gerontological societies in many countries of Europe and of the first societies in the United States and Argentina. The funds for travel and other obligations in this work came in part from the Ciba Pharmaceutical Company and in part from Lord Nuffield, the "Henry Ford" of Great Britain.

"Next summer," Doctor Korenchevsky told us, "some of our efforts will be rewarded. The First International Congress of Gerontology will be held in Liège. Doctor Brull, in that city, has been working with me, and we now have the support of many interested persons in England, Belgium and other countries."

As events turned out, the enthusiasm which went into the setting up of this congress was well-founded, for it was there that the International Association of Gerontology came into existence. There, too, Doctor Korenchevsky's stimulating role was recognized by the passing of a special motion to create him a permanent member of the governing body of the International Association. Two years later, when the meeting of the Association was held in St. Louis, Missouri, Korenchevsky was active in the setting up of an International Research Committee to deal specifically with the biological and medical problems of aging. But at the time of our visit these happenings were still in the future. Our host spoke with great conviction of the strides in research which might be made with organization—and money. "In the United States," he said, "you have remarkable potentialities. Your Public Health Service, I understand, will have a half million dollars to devote to studies on aging in the hospitals of

Baltimore and elsewhere." There was a wistful tone to his voice, that seemed somehow to me to express the hope of scientists in many small laboratories, struggling forward in their labors on meager budgets, that some day a little more of the vast wealth of the world would be channeled into the fields of basic research. The time of our departure was approaching and Doctor Korenchevsky drove us to the station, leaving his assistant in charge at the laboratory. Right up until the moment that our train was ready to leave Oxford, he talked of research and of the unsolved problems before us.

During his work in Russia, Korenchevsky published fifteen papers and one book. In England, he had published 138 papers and a book. His refinement of the theories of autointoxication as a cause of aging, in which protein metabolites of the endogenous metabolism of the body eventually have an injurious effect on cells and tissues, is an outstanding concept in modern gerontology. His practical studies on the treatment of hormone deficiencies in old people and on the impracticability of treating aging *as such* with sex or other hormones, will mean much to the physician dealing with aged patients. His influence, however, in the stimulation of other investigators, singly and in groups, has extended far beyond the realm even of these productive personal accomplishments.

＊　＊　＊

One anecdote which our host recounted remains vividly in my memory. It concerned the great physiologist, I. P. Pavlov, who had been a source of inspiration in Korenchevsky's early work:

At the Petrograd Institute of Experimental Medicine Pavlov permitted his disciples to ask him nonscientific questions during only one hour, at lunchtime. During one of these lunchhours, a young French scientist asked him, in a somewhat naive manner, how one could become a great scientist "like Professor Pavlov." Without smiling, the professor replied: "This is very easy indeed. When you awake in the morning, begin to think about your research. As you shave and bathe, continue to think about it. Do not stop thinking about it while you are eating breakfast. Concentrate upon your investigative work on your way to the laboratory. You will find that you can train yourself to automatic avoidance of the traffic when you are crossing the street. Then, of course, while you are in the laboratory, continue to concentrate. When you go to bed at night, dream of your research problems. Yes, it is very easy."

I do not know how well the French scientist followed Professor Pavlov's precepts. But Vladimir Korenchevsky surely has followed them faithfully in his lifelong devotion to research on the great problems of the aging process.

Chapter 6

AT THE FOOT OF THE ALPS

A Visit to Italy's Leading Microscopist

AS THE GENEVA-TO-ROME express rolled swiftly along, I sat back and closed my eyes. I was thinking of something which had happened a great many miles away, in Montevideo, Uruguay, to be exact, and a number of years earlier. It was there, in a little bookshop, that I had purchased a Spanish translation of the work of the great Italian histologist, Giuseppe Levi. For it was in this faraway country of Latin America that I had come to a new realization of the marvellous accomplishments of the men of Spain and Italy who had devoted themselves to unravelling the intricacies of the minute structure of the body and, in particular, of the most intricate mechanism of all—the nervous system. In the tradition of their devoted efforts, the modern genius of Italian histology, Giuseppe Levi, had carried on. It was no wonder, then, that I turned the richly illustrated pages of his ample treatise with something akin to reverence and carried it from the shop with a sense of having just discovered a treasure.

❊ ❊ ❊

I opened my eyes. The imposing mountain scenery was literally flying past us. And now we were coming ever closer to Turin and another rendevous with greatness—we were on our way to visit the laboratory of Giuseppe Levi!

From Culoz we had passed through the grandest mountain scenery of our experience. We seemed to be in the very midst of the snow-capped giants. Tall forests of pine rose upon either side, and the cascades of sparkling mountain streams fell almost

FIGURE 11 Giuseppe Levi.

vertically from high above. The peaks were lower now but still very rugged and imposing. We were passing through a valley walled by the foothills of the Italian Alps. Suddenly a different type of shape arose above the ruggedness of the hills—the bulk of a huge castle, straight from the Middle Ages. We kept it in view for a long time. Indeed, it must have commanded a vast stretch of the country and been a guardian for many hamlets and lesser fortifications. It was the Castle of Avigliane, and for us, our first such reminder of the feudal age of Europe.

Still in sight of the majestic hills, we drew into the outskirts of Turin and in a short time were at the central railroad station. Here the ugly wounds of World War II were clearly visible, for large segments of the terminal building had suffered from the heavy allied bombing at Turin. We secured a porter and walked the few short blocks to our hotel—the Principe di Piemonte.

Turin, the modern city, is an industrial metropolis of over half a million inhabitants, the chief manufacturing site for motor cars in Italy and the home of many other manufacturing activities. Its history, however, goes far back into the past of Italy and of the Roman domain. For a time in the nineteenth century it was the capital of Italy. Earlier, it had been a prize which changed hands between the French and the Italians. It was at Turin in 1706 that Eugene of Savoy, in a great battle, finally broke the French power in northern Italy. His army was greatly aided in routing the foreign army by the Turinese themselves.

Our chambers were high above the street level, and from them the vista of the rugged hills again appeared and, in the distance, even the great bulk of the Castle of Avigliane. We had begun unpacking when the telephone rang. It was Giuseppe Levi himself, and he was in the lobby to greet us. I left Nancy to relax a little from the long train ride and went down to meet the professor. He rose from a chair as I entered the lobby. Levi was a tall, well-proportioned man with a majestic head and a face of such length as to give a sense of persistent solemnity. His iron gray hair was short and somewhat frizzled. All in all, had he been dressed in a toga rather than a modern suit, I might have been facing a senator of Rome. After a hospitable greeting, he asked if I would chat awhile here and if Nancy and I would both come to his laboratory in the morning.

He spoke warmly of my professor at Yale, Ross Granville Harrison, of Doctor Edmund V. Cowdry, at Washington University and of other friends of his in the States. Professor Levi has had a particular reason for appreciating the friendship of scientists of other lands. Devoted almost wholly to his scientific studies, he has said of himself, "I never took any interest in politics and always wished to ignore any activity implying my participation in public life. I was, however, definitely against the fascist regime cn account of its cramping effect on freedom of thought and its lowering of human dignity." Courageously, Doctor Levi spoke out against the evils of fascist rule. In 1934 he was imprisoned. From his scientific friends, including Harrison of Yale, Streeter of the Carnegie Institute, Ramón y Cajal of Madrid and many others, came declarations of dissent which even Mussolini felt it better not to ignore. After two months he was released. Thus again the impact of political forces is seen in the life of a man whose great desire was complete devotion to scientific work and achievement.

In the course of our conversation, Levi mentioned the book *General Cytology*, published first in Spanish in Argentina and written by Eduardo De Robertis, an ambitious and enthusiastic young cytologist of that country, together with Francisco A. Saez, the cytogeneticist of La Plata, and Wiktor W. Nowinski, a brilliant cyto and biochemist, originally from Poland, who was working then in the Argentine. I recently had completed an English translation, published by Saunders of Philadelphia, of this work, and Professor Levi was kind in his comments concerning it. This discussion led him into what to me was a fascinating expression of his personal opinions on some aspects of modern research. Here was his statement, more or less in his own words: "I regard the growing tendency among young workers to follow 'fashionable trends' as a danger for scientific progress. This means to me an abdication of one's own personality, caused by the fear of being old-fashioned. I shall give you an example. Histochemistry is now much up-to-date. I do not contest that this discipline is going to have a future. Many young people, however, confine themselves exclusively to histochemical investigations, neglecting a number of problems which should have been solved long ago."

Of the tendency to overspecialization, he quoted the words of the great Claude Bernard, written a century ago: "There exist two orders of specialties in science: a necessary one, i.e., technique, and a harmful one, i.e., culture." The specialization which is made necessary by the rapid development and complexity of scientific research should not constrain to too great a degree the inquiring mind which poses the question, at first, perhaps, without even a settled attitude as to what technique shall be used to answer it.

Our hour had sped swiftly away. Professor Levi bade me goodbye. The late afternoon was passed with a short stroll on the streets of Turin. It was our first Italian city, and we were somewhat surprised at the general aspect of things, for there was an air of prosperity, with throngs of well-dressed and apparently cheerful people and with handsomely decorated and well-stocked shop windows. One certainly could not see evidences here of a conquered nation nor of occupied territory.

Next morning we were up early. After a continental breakfast with hot chocolate and rolls, we took a tram, as I had been directed by Professor Levi, to the Institute of Anatomy. The Institute is on a broad tree-lined avenue, and from the exterior it reminded one more of a great old private mansion than of a scientific laboratory. A porter admitted us to the quiet, cool atmosphere within its walls and led us upstairs to the office of the "master."

Professor Levi, in his long workcoat, seemed very much a part of the laboratory, with its blended air of classical tradition and of busy activity. He soon had us peering through microscopes at some of the most beautiful preparations which we ever had seen. These were made from tissue cultures of nerve cells, taken from spinal ganglia and kept alive for days or weeks outside of the body. They had been stained with silver by the intricate methods for which Spanish and Italian histologists are famous, and the marvellous complexity of the cells, with their many branching processes, was brought out in all of its detail. After discussing some of the many problems which had been studied in the laboratory, I asked Levi about a group picture which hung near his desk. "These," he told me, indicating each man in turn, "are von Kölliker, Golgi, Bizzozero and Perroncito."

It was a list which would widen the eyes of any student of microscopic anatomy. Albrecht von Kölliker, Swiss scientist, had been the first to write a formal treatise on microscopic anatomy *and* the first to write such a treatise on comparative embryology. After work in his native Zürich, he had gone to Germany to study with the great Johannes Müller.

Camillo Golgi, Italian scientist, had made remarkable advances in the staining of the nervous tissue. His laboratory at Pavia had been a training ground for many renowned workers. In 1906, he had shared the Nobel prize in medicine with Ramón y Cajal. The other two, Bizzozero and Perroncito, had contributed greatly to the progress of our knowledge of microscopic structure. Such men Levi had come to know at scientific congresses in many of the cities of Europe. His own training had brought him into more intimate contact with some of the greatest scholars of the past century, both in his country and abroad. When he entered upon the study of medicine in 1889, he was very young, not yet seventeen years of age. While still a student, he met the young Gino Galeotti at the Institute of General Pathology, a man whose great intellectual capacity and enthusiasm helped greatly to turn Levi toward the field of scientific research for its own sake. Graduating in 1895, he became an assistant in the Clinical Hospital for Nervous and Mental Diseases in Florence. Here good fortune brought him into con-

FIGURE 12   The Royal Palace at Turin, Italy. The mounted figures represent the gods Castor and Pollux.

tact with Ernesto Lugaro, "a passionate investigator in the histology of the nervous system." This was another factor in the "bending of the twig." After three years of such work, Doctor Levi's decision was made; he would devote himself wholly to the study of microscopic anatomy. For further training, he journeyed to Berlin to enter the Anatomical-Biological Institute directed by the outstanding biologist, Oskar Hertwig. Here he remained for a year.

Back in Florence, Levi became assistant at the Institute of Anatomy, under the fine morphologist and embryologist, Ciulio Chiarugi. During this time he made important studies on the comparative histology and the development of nervous tissue, which had a marked influence on his later theoretical work in relation to the aging process.

It was in 1915 at the University of Palermo, in Sicily, that Levi was introduced to a field in which he was to carry on for over forty years. This was the relatively new realm of tissue culture—the growing of living cells outside of the body. This work was temporarily interrupted while "Major Levi" served at the battle front in 1916-17, but resumed with great vigor when he was given the professorship of anatomy at Turin in 1919. The preparations which we just had been examining in his laboratory were, however, from some of his more recent experiments using the methods of tissue culture. Before leaving his office, I noted a copy of his classical Italian text on histology, the Spanish translation of which I purchased in faraway Montevideo. In this book, Professor Levi presents histology more from a biological aspect than is seen in our own English and American texts on the subject, stressing general principles and using examples of tissue structure and function from many animal forms.

We now descended to the library of the Institute. A feature of many departments and institutes in Europe is a fine individual library in the special field concerned. This system has certain advantages, it must be admitted, in placing the literature closer to the laboratory than when it is in a central library. Among the many interesting items was a book inscribed with a dedication to Levi by the Spanish master, Ramón y Cajal, dated 1934. In this book Cajal also had put in his own handwriting the famous formula of De Castro for the staining of nerve cells.

We sat down to chat for awhile. I asked Doctor Levi about the support of his research, always a subject of interest among investigators of modern times. Under the fascist regime, it was a hard struggle for a man with Levi's love of freedom and his frankness of attitude. Financial aid was cut off both from the government research council and from the academic authorities. "The work of our Institute would have been severely crippled but for the Rockefeller Foundation which came to the rescue and aided with funds until 1938," he told us.

In 1939, Doctor Levi, in his years of study of the nervous tissue, had discovered numerous new facts, and it was a fascinating opportunity to talk about them in this personal manner. He pointed out how the tissue culture method which he and his associates had used had allowed nerve cells to grow to enormous size in some cases, since the inhibiting factors of growth within the body had been removed. He had shown also how nerve cells will regenerate their processes, even in tissue culture, and that these processes themselves, cut off from the cell, will live for several hours and even show ameboid motion at both ends! In animals which seem to grow throughout the life span, as in fishes and turtles, Levi found that the nerve cells which, unlike other cells, do not *multiply*, continue to grow in size and reach gigantic proportions. Another contribution which Professor Levi has made is his insistence that the minute cell organelles, known as mitochondria, are stable elements and do not transform, as so many early workers thought, into secretion granules, fat droplets or other materials.

Professor Levi spoke with affection of the many disciples who had worked under him and now were carrying on their own research in many parts of the world. Some of them, like Rita Levi-Montalcini, at Washington University in St. Louis, and Herta Meyer, at the Institute of Biology in Rio de Janeiro, I had come to know in recent years through personal visits to their places of work. Doctor Levi's attitude toward his pupils was of much interest to me. He did not wish to take credit for their successful, often brilliant, careers in science. "If there be some merit of mine in this regard," he says, "it has been in selecting young disciples who were steady workers and, above all, entertained a sincere love for scientific research, attended by no little abnegation, too, as financial conditions for university assistants are far from brilliant in Italy; they can hardly make a living." He has always tried to establish cordial relations, sometimes even deep friendships, with his coworkers. His advice and counsel have been given unstintingly. "But," he says, "I always left them quite free to investigate the field they liked best." In these days of highly organized research, this is a refreshing attitude!

As we arose to take our leave, Professor Levi accompanied us to the door. We were almost reluctant to quit this cool realm of science and of selfless research.

This has been the salient thought which returns to me when I recall Professor Levi and our visit to his laboratory in Turin— the humbleness and disinterestedness of the true scientist. One of Professor Levi's favorite aphorisms is that of the sage of India, Dhammapada. It reads:

> As a massive rock is not shaken by the wind,
> Neither is the Wise by blame or praise.

Chapter 7

PERROS AND PERON

A Visit to Professor Bernardo Houssay

O N THE evening before, we had boarded the overnight boat bound from Montevideo to Buenos Aires. A pleasant excursion it was, with the passengers seeming to have something of the free detached air which so often goes along with travel by ship, even though this is but a short trip. The boat takes one along the broad Rio de la Plata from the metropolis of Uruguay to the metropolis of Argentina in an evening and a night.

We had stayed up fairly late, watching the games, strolling on the deck and observing the throngs of passengers. As the lights of the city faded behind us, the majestic scenery of the southern sky opened out above us. The Southern Cross now shone forth more brilliantly than I ever had seen it, and a number of other constellations, strange to us of the northern hemisphere, vied with it. Finally, we left the rail and retired, to be lulled to sleep by the gentle motion of the waves.

Although we had been at work in Montevideo for the past two months, this was to be our first visit to Buenos Aires, and we rolled out of our bunks early in the morning with a sense of real anticipation. The anticipation was heightened by the fact that our plans for our stay in this new country included a visit to the greatest of Argentine physiologists—Bernardo Alberto Houssay.

Since the beginning of my scientific studies in the graduate schools of Brown University and Yale University, this name had been a familiar one to me. Houssay was known for his produc-

73

FIGURE 13 Bernardo Houssay.

tivity, seen in the great volume of the scientific publication which came from his laboratory, and for thoroughness, demonstrated in the hard, clear logic of the planning which went into his experimental studies.

We dressed and had a light breakfast, the continental one of rolls and coffee to which we had become accustomed in Latin

America. It was still very early morning as we stood at the rail, waiting for our first glimpse of Buenos Aires. We struck up a conversation with a fellow passenger. Our stay in Montevideo had helped to rub some of the rough edges from our Castilian, and we were now enjoying such opportunities.

"This is our first visit to Buenos Aires," I said. "But we have heard and read a great deal about it." Our companion was a man of some travel experience. "You will find it somewhat like your own great cities," he said, "but probably more like Paris." This stopped me momentarily, for the comparison, while it turned out later to be a good one, did not mean very much to us. At that time we had never been to Paris! Now the horizon began to show the summits of lofty buildings, and soon we were in full sight of the metropolis. It was indeed a beautiful and impressive sight—not the awe-inspiring skyline of Manhattan, but still a great and thoroughly modern city. The ship pulled into its dock amid scenes of great enthusiasm. There were many on shore to greet the passengers, and the trip across the Rio de la Plata seemed to be of as much importance to many of these voyagers and their relatives as might a transatlantic sailing.

We were surprised at the easy passage through customs. In fact, the officials did not even examine our passports. Perhaps, we thought, the seriousness of the political situation in Argentina had been overemphasized. We had heard a few months before how a young army officer named Juan Peron had risen rapidly to a very powerful position. At that time he not only held the positions of Minister of War and of Labor but also was Vice-President. It was actually his fellow officers who had become concerned about his growing power and his lack of scruples. They had ordered his arrest, and when he and his companion, Eva Duarte, fled from Buenos Aires, he was apprehended and actually did spend some time in a military prison. The frantic efforts of his Eva and those of many influential friends had caused him to be freed. He had made a public appearance and in a dramatic gesture declared his devotion to the cause of the *descamisados,* the "shirtless ones," or, more accurately, the poor and toiling masses.

Such a sequence of events naturally had made him a hero in the eyes of many. At the same time, the government itself was in a state of weakness and vacillation. The leaders of the various parties could not agree on appointments to the cabinet, and confusion was rapidly becoming compounded. The time was ripe for the entrance of a strong man.

Once on land, we took a taxi to the Hotel Continental. After resting a hour or so, we had breakfast. I planned to contact that first day Doctor Eduardo DeRobertis, then Assistant Professor of Microscopic Anatomy at the Medical School of the University of Buenos Aires. We had many mutual friends and had corresponded, but we had never met. First, however, we thought, we might explore the city. We walked out along the Avenue Presidente Roque Saenz Peña y Esmeralda and to Corrientes. Buenos Aires is truly a metropolis, even then a city of over two and a half million persons, by far the largest in the southern hemisphere. The streets were thronged with well-dressed people and there was an aspect, in general, of sleek well being. Such an appearance, however, might have been due, to some extent, to the customs of the country, for walking without coat or tie on these main avenues is hardly thinkable, except for the laboring class. We entered some of the shops. One, in particular, a huge bookstore, intrigued us. Here were thousands of fine books, most of them printed and bound in Argentina. One enormous work concerned the *Plants of Argentina* and sold for 350 pesos (about ninety dollars).

We returned to the hotel for lunch. Then we continued our exploration, this time walking up the broad Avenida de Mayo to the Plaza del Congreso. This is the very center of Argentine government—in this sense it is like our capitol hill. However, there is no hill, only a wide square with the imposing dome of the congress building rising on one side of it.

On the large square at the other end of the Avenida is the beautiful Casa Rosada—the Rose House or Pink House, which, like our White House, is the official residence of the President of the Republic. As we walked on these wide avenues and looked at the impressive buildings and monuments of the city,

I realized that I was in the greatest city of the Spanish-speaking world—the heir of the rich culture of Spain, once the most powerful country on earth, and at the same time a city with the bustle and hurry of its sisters to the north—of New York, Chicago or others of our own great cities.

For the return to our hotel, we made our first venture on the Argentine subway and found it as efficient as those of New York and a bit more decorative, with beautifully tiled walls at each station. That evening I called DeRobertis. He expressed great pleasure at our actually being in Buenos Aires and said that he would call for me about 9 A.M. the next day. He was to take me to the medical school and later to present me to Doctor Houssay.

*　*　*

To say that I was not prepared for the School of Medicine of the National University of Buenos Aires would be putting it mildly. A magnificent building, nineteen stories in height, greeted my eyes. DeRobertis led me through a door into a spacious hall. Magnificent pillars of some type of highly polished black stone formed an avenue through which we walked to a bank of elevators. Entering one of these, we were whisked swiftly and quietly to an upper floor. Here was the Institute of Histology and Embryology. The laboratories were provided with some of the most modern types of equipment which included a freezing-drying apparatus for the rapid preparation, with minimum change, of tissues for study under the microscope and a spectrophotometer to analyse the chemical substances within tissues by the manner in which they absorb light rays. Doctor DeRobertis explained to me some of the problems which were under study. His own work on the secretion by the cells of the thyroid gland, work which has since become classical, was of special interest to me. "We have identified in the follicles of the gland," he told me, "a protein-splitting enzyme which actually digests the colloid stored there so that it can be passed back into the blood stream to control the metabolism of the entire body." It was particularly significant for me to hear this, since in one of my own papers a few years before I had *theorized* that such an enzyme should exist in the thyroid gland.

DeRobertis now took me to the office of Doctor Manuel E. Varela, who described to me in detail the teaching methods and materials. A full month was spent at the beginning of the course in the study of fresh tissues and of single-celled animals, a method which we had thought of in our own country as being a very progressive technique of teaching.

As we left the school of medicine, I was thinking of what a fine future seemed in store for Eduardo DeRobertis, both in regard to the research opportunities which I had just seen and to the fact that he was the likely successor to Professor Varela as director of the Institute. I mentioned to him some of these thoughts, thinking it only a pleasant topic of conversation. His handsome face darkened. "The future is very unclear for us here in Argentina," he said. "If Peron is elected President . . ." He left the sentence unfinished, but I could sense the menace that the coming struggle held. It was but a few weeks until election, and a confident Peron was putting all possible weight into the campaign.

"Now," said DeRobertis, "we can at least show our opposition." He turned the label of his coat toward me. There was a bright coin—a five centesimo piece. "This means," he said, "unyielding resistance to encroachments on our political liberties. But it is becoming more and more dangerous to make known one's opposition to the 'Peronistas'."

We walked a short distance and stopped before a large building, an edifice that was quite different from the gleaming school of medicine which we had just left. This building obviously had once been a fine private house, but its state of repair at present left something to be desired. I knew also that private houses are not easily converted into modern scientific laboratories, as I had experienced some problems of this type in our own country.

"Here we are," said DeRobertis. "This is the Institute of Biology and Experimental Medicine, and here we shall find the man of whom you have heard so much—Professor Bernardo Houssay!"

Again, it would not be an exaggeration to say that I was

totally unprepared for what we encountered within this building. The unprepossessing exterior had given no indication of the carefully planned utilization of the space within. We walked down a long hall from which laboratories opened on either side and entered the office of the director.

Professor Houssay rose as we came in, and DeRobertis presented me to him. Bernardo Houssay was an impressive figure of a man. Of medium height, but of unusually erect attitude, he presented an aspect of a man of great physical resources—an air of freshness and "springiness," which became more impressive the longer that one was with him. His aristocratic features, broad forehead and neat moustache gave an appearance of intellectuality consistent with his long record of high scientific achievement. He asked me to be seated. He was interested in my work in Montevideo, and it was not too easy to lead the conversation toward his own studies and particularly toward the recent past with its far-from-pleasant aspects. Yet I did want to know more of the details of what had occurred and of what the political ordeals of Argentina had meant to academic men such as Houssay. Before we had talked much further, however, Houssay said, "Come, let us take a little tour of the laboratories. Perhaps you will see some things which will interest you." We went from room to room, the professor explaining briefly, but with great clarity, the type of work carried on in each. The complicated experimental studies of Doctor Houssay, his colleagues and assistants, require a variety of techniques and equipment. Some rooms were for physiological studies on dogs, others for experimental surgery (under precautions easily as great as those for human beings), others for biochemical preparation and assay, and still others were the living quarters of the experimental animals. Everywhere the importance of *los perros,* "the dogs," was emphasized to me. To Professor Houssay and the others, these were not mere dumb beasts to be studied only to satisfy man's curiosity. They were experimental subjects, almost sacred objects, the welfare of which was of tremendous importance to the experimenter. They were creatures which, except for the necessities of scientific investigation, were to be treated with every possible care and consideration.

Indeed, if one considers how much has been contributed to human knowledge by studies on the dog and how greatly the practice of medicine and surgery have profited by such studies, *el perro* does seem to be described truly as man's best friend. With the dog to aid him in the laboratory, man has unravelled the mysteries of conditioned reflexes, has solved the problems of complicated functions in the digestive, circulatory, nervous and other systems of the body, has investigated the effects of hundreds of kinds of medicines and drugs and has accomplished a multitude of other scientific tasks. And in spite of the polemics of the anti-vivisectionists, the work has been done with a minimum of suffering, for, in fact, it has been and still is carried out by men whose chief aim in life is to prevent or alleviate suffering. In the attitude of Doctor Houssay and the others toward these experimental dogs, one could see almost the attitude of a doctor toward his patients, when he knows that a few words of kindness and encouragement, whether in English or in Spanish, can help to alleviate temporary suffering or inconvenience.

FIGURE 14   Model figures from Argentina. These well-made lead toys represent a bull and a sturdy gaucho of the pampas.

The work of Houssay has by no means been confined to studies on the dog, for in particular experiments he has used rats, guinea pigs and other mammals, and for special studies he has gone to cold-blooded vertebrates, such as frogs and toads, which usually are kept available in large tanks in the laboratories of the Institute.

We returned now to his office. It was in the discussion of the facilities of the building that our conversation found its way rather easily to those events which led to its occupation. "I had been a member of the faculty of the medical school for twenty-four years," Doctor Houssay said, "when, in 1943, I joined with others to protest against the increasingly reactionary and un-democratic nature of the government." This was before the name of Peron had become a prominent one, but the fascist tendencies of the groups to which he belonged were already becoming only too evident. "There were one hundred and fifty of us," Doctor Houssay continued, "who signed a petition publicly demanding that the government adhere to democratic principles. Our names were there for all to see."

The revenge of the government was not long in coming. The method was more subtle than have been some of those of the modern totalitarians, but nonetheless effective and brutal. A law was passed making it possible for the government to retire any academic person who had reached the age of fifty-five years. The rest was simple. Professor Houssay and the other "enemies of the state" were asked to leave the positions in which they had served so long and well. It was, indeed, only good fortune that private support was obtainable to permit the setting up of the Institute of Experimental Biology and Medicine and the continuation of the long-range experiments of Doctor Houssay. "It has not been too bad," the professor was saying. "At least, we have been able to work here." And in this he certainly was amply supported by the activity which I had seen in the laboratories and by the scientific papers which still were continuing to appear in an uninterrupted stream.

What manner of man was this Bernardo Houssay who seemed so completely devoted to his science and who still would risk his future of productive work, his reputation and even his life itself to protest against the growing tyranny of the new government? Of him our own great physiologist, Walter B. Cannon, of Harvard, had said, ". . . one of the most outstanding contributors to science in the whole South American continent." Indeed, Houssay at that time already had trained a host of disciples who had spread his influence widely. Three of these had come to Harvard, while several Harvard investigators had gone to him in Buenos Aires for inspiration and for special training. He had been elected to the American Philosophical Society of Philadelphia and the National Academy of Sciences of Washington, D.C. At the tercentenary celebration of Harvard University, he had been the recipient of a Doctor of Science degree. He holds honorary degrees in science also from Oxford, Columbia, New York, Mexico and São Paulo; in medicine, from Paris, Brussels, Louvain, Strasbourg, Lyons, Geneva, Montreal, the Catholic University of Chile, Asuncion, Rio de Janeiro and Montevideo, and in law, from the University of Glasgow. The other honors which he has received from scientific societies all over the world would fill several pages. These things I did not learn directly from Professor Houssay, but from other sources, for one of his outstanding traits is personal modesty.

Of his work itself, however, he was willing to talk. While I had read of his experiments on the endocrine glands and in particular on the role of the pituitary gland in diabetes, it is more thrilling to have even a short personal conversation with a scientist concerning his work than to read numerous papers describing it—and it is sometimes more illuminating. The thrill would have been even greater at this time had I known that less than two years later this work was to lead him to the crowning honor of his life: the Nobel prize in medicine for 1947!

A little coincidence which amused us was that Houssay's early ambition, after reading *Lives of the Saints,* had been to become a missionary. I, too, had an identical ambition as a boy, but apparently we both had been detracted by the muse of science.

From what I learned that afternoon and later, the wide

cultural background of Houssay was almost as impressive as were his scientific accomplishments. His father, a Frenchman, was a lawyer, a man of broad culture and phenomenal memory, who was well-read in the Latin and Greek, as well as in the French and Spanish classics. Bernardo was born in Buenos Aires. At five years of age, he had begun to read. He read widely in the French and Spanish literature and history. He speaks with deep gratitude of the kindness of both of his parents. His mother contributed to his character a love for moral uprightness and for perseverance. Yet, at thirteen years of age, he decided to follow his studies with no further help from his parents and he succeeded in doing so. "I early was convinced that fundamental research in basic sciences is the source of all progress in applied sciences, such as technology, public health and the practice of medicine. I came to realize also that a *broad* culture is of great importance for a scientist." He gives much credit to the classical lecture by Claude Bernard, "Introduction a l' Étude de la Médicine Experimental," which made a particularly strong impression upon his own work.

Houssay's life has been an amazing story of accomplishment. A bachelor at thirteen years, pharmacist at seventeen, and a doctor of medicine at twenty-two, he became a full professor at twenty-three years of age! He has worked constantly for academic freedom and the progress of science in his native Argentina and in the other countries of Latin America, and not a few times the struggle has been not only a difficult but also a dangerous one.

It was growing late in the afternoon, and we felt it time to take our leave. "You will honor me by bringing your señora to a fiesta at our home this evening," said Doctor Houssay. "It is a very significant occasion—our boda de plata—our 'silver wedding anniversary'." It was in truth *I* who was honored by the invitation.

Back at the Hotel Continental, I told Nancy of our good fortune. We decided to rest awhile in preparation for the event. It was only a few moments after we had lain down that the quiet was broken by a commotion in the street beneath our windows.

At first we tried to ignore it, but as the sounds grew in volume and angry cries and shouts arose, we went to the open windows and looked out. The narrow street on this side of our hotel was a scene of confusion and violence. Evidently, an attempt had been made to hold a meeting in this avenue, which was closed off to traffic during certain hours. There were hundreds of civilians, mostly young men. A police car had just arrived, and uniformed men were rushing in with clubs to disperse the crowds. The tactics of the anti-Peronists seemed to be to fall back, then to attempt to gather again and to give blow for blow whenever the odds seemed even. But now more police cars were racing into the crowded street, some closed and of ominous appearance. As the police on foot began to fall back, an unpleasant odor filled the air. Some type of noxious gas was being used to break up the crowds!

Suddenly, we saw small groups and single individuals from among the anti-Peronistas dashing forward—directly into the gas-filled areas. Each person carried a crumpled newspaper and set a match to it as he ran. And now from the windows of adjoining buildings many burning newspapers descended into the street, floating like fiery angels toward the scene of conflict. An acrid odor filled the air. The ignited newspapers were consuming the gas discharged from the police cars. We closed our windows and, somewhat shaken, retired into the room. The tumult outside continued, but gradually became more subdued, and no shots had been fired.

We dressed and went to the front of the hotel, where all was surprisingly calm. We took a taxi to the home of Professor Houssay.

The distinguished, but not elaborate, home of the Houssays was the scene this evening of a really festive occasion. Flowers were everywhere. The hallway, the broad stairs leading to the second floor and the rooms of the first floor were filled with basket upon basket of varied blossoms. Their delicious fragrance seemed to fill the house. In every room were guests—professional and personal acquaintances of the Houssays—and very many relatives, for these Latin Americans prize the bonds of relationship.

We were ushered through the outer rooms and presented to Professor Houssay and the gracious Señora de Houssay, then in quick succession introduced to one after another of the guests. There was no apparent anxiety here, or at least none that we could detect, concerning the serious political situation. Here there was only a dignified gaiety. Champagne was abundant, and many varieties of food were served during the evening.

We spent some time in the library, which was as well-filled with guests as were the other rooms. But here, between the evening dresses, suits and uniforms, I was able to see some of the host's fine collections of books and at least a portion of the multitude of diplomas and certificates of honor which had been bestowed upon him.

Late in the evening we said goodbye to the Professor and Señora Houssay. "Perhaps when you come again to Argentina," Professor Houssay said, "the future will seem more bright for our country."

But back in our hotel room, we heard, far into the night, shouting in the streets of Buenos Aires. There were to be many anxious months and years for the lovers of freedom in that unfortunate country before the return of democracy.

Chapter 8

AN ENGLISH PRESIDENT

A Visit to Doctor W. J. Hamilton, President of the British Association of Anatomists

AMONG our friends who attended the meeting of the American Association of Anatomists each year was Doctor Harland Mossman. I knew him as a fine anatomist, a charming conversationalist and a person of somewhat unusual background, one whose name was associated with international cooperation in our field of science. A book on the development of the human body had been written by two English anatomists and Doctor Mossman, and this text, under the name of *Hamilton, Boyd and Mossman,* was well known and widely used in the United States. It was natural, therefore, that I sought him out at the 1954 meeting of our Association in Galveston, Texas, to ask his advice about our proposed stay in England and the Netherlands. His comments about the anatomical laboratories and collections in both countries were to be of much help to us, but of even more benefit was his own personal association with the English and Dutch anatomists. Before we sailed for England, then, a visit to his good friend, Doctor William J. Hamilton, Professor of Anatomy at Charing Cross Hospital Medical School, was high on our agenda. Anticipation of the visit was not lessened when we learned that Hamilton was at that time serving as president of the British Association of Anatomists!

It was not long after the close of the sessions of the International Association of Gerontology that I telephoned Professor Hamilton. He invited us to come to his department the very next day.

FIGURE 15   William J. Hamilton.

Nancy and I went by cab to the Charing Cross Hospital Medical School. Incidentally, the ancient term "cross", as in Charing Cross, Banbury Cross and others, did refer in each case to an actual monument erected in the area which served as a landmark when "addresses" of buildings were in a very hazy state of development.

The medical school, like most of those in Great Britain, was in close association with the hospital from which it derived its name. It was an ancient, but not very imposing structure. The interior, however, showed all the marks of being an up-to-date institution of medical education. As the secretary led us into Doctor Hamilton's office, he rose and greeted us pleasantly. Doctor Hamilton was a tall man of early middle age with a sturdy frame and proudly erect posture. His blond hair was cut close. His face was smooth shaven and formed a long oval, but his chin jutted forward just enough to remind one of the pugnacity of a John Bull. He was dressed in the costume of our trade, a long white laboratory coat.

He beckoned us to chairs, and we relaxed for a little discussion of mutual friends and interests before beginning a tour of the department. He spoke warmly of Doctor Mossman and of how they had become acquainted while both were in Boyd's department at Cambridge University. It was there that the plan for *Embryology* had been formed.

As we talked, I could not help noticing the good sense of order and arrangement reflected in the office. Only too often the "lair" of a scientist is portrayed as a scene of confusion, where specimens, books and equipment are piled on desks, tables and chairs in great disarray. Here, the scene was quite the reverse, with filing cabinets neatly labelled, work in progress in orderly stacks, and when there was need for reference, an obvious knowledge both on the part of Doctor Hamilton and of his efficient secretary, Miss Bennett, of where to find the needed information.

Indeed, our conversation did lead to a need to refer to several kinds of data. Doctor Hamilton was telling us of the importance of the Central Research Committee of London University in the work of the medical colleges. "You see," he said, "all of the medical schools here actually are parts of London University. The Central Research Committee studies their needs and their requests and makes available to them generous sums of money for scientific investigation." He took from a file a booklet with detailed budgetary data on the London medical schools and gave it to me. "You may keep it if you wish," he said.

I told him a little about the subject of research grants in the United States, knowing that he already was aware of the general system but giving him examples. "Since I myself began to teach and carry on research in the fields of anatomy and medicine, some fifteen years ago, the importance of this grant system has increased tremendously," I told him. "Up until about that time the support of research work was pretty largely a matter for the administration of the medical school where the investigator was employed. Since his teaching responsibilities were there, the school felt an obligation to help him in his investigations, to purchase for him experimental animals, laboratory supplies and equipment of various kinds. For the more experienced man, an assistant or two might be employed by the school to help him with the preparation of specimens or in other ways. As the private foundations, the United States Public Health Service and the Armed Forces began to offer more support or at least to consider applications for support, the medical schools, already burdened with increasing costs of medical education, very willingly began to cut down on the budget allocations for research. In some schools, the amount now is little or, practically speaking, nothing."

Doctor Hamilton told me that it would be wrong to think that the British medical schools did not have any source of grants from outside funds, such as those private foundations; but the solid and substantial support was still an intramural affair. He now spoke of a difference between the teaching of anatomy in American and British schools which, he said, had been very surprising to him when he first learned of it. In the British Isles, the anatomists are physicians, and each one is carefully and thoroughly trained in the gross structure of the human body. He has a type of knowledge which can be gained only by precise dissection of its various parts. In the United States, on the other hand, the leading anatomists in a number of the medical schools have little knowledge of this type. The increasing stress laid in anatomy on certain supposedly modern and up-to-date types of research has led to an attainment of prominence by anatomists who have opportunely entered upon such research, who have perhaps worked in frontier areas between microscopic anatomy and chemistry or who have had available new and expensive equipment such as the electron microscope.

"Why," said Doctor Hamilton, "I have heard the chairman

of an anatomy department of a great university in your mid-west actually boasts that he *never* had dissected a human body!" It was an interesting point of difference and one of which I had been somewhat aware, but I could see clearly now how paradoxical such a situation would seem to a British anatomist.

Like many a professor of a basic science in a medical school, Professor Hamilton was active in the work of the Admissions Committee, which has the duty of considering applicants for the study of medicine. Since I had just been serving as chairman of that committee in our own institution, I was particularly interested in comparing notes. He told me that applicants, besides furnishing complete records of their previous work, were invited for personal interviews with members of the committee, a method of assessment very common, of course, in industry. It cannot be denied that the applicant often is under some tension at such time, for the number who can be accepted is relatively small compared to those who are beating at the doors. Doctor Hamilton told me that at Charing Cross some 300 interviews are held every year in selecting a class of forty-five students.

Other interesting points of similarity in the problems of admission to medical schools here and at home included the pressure which anxious and influential parents sometimes attempted to bring to bear to have their sons admitted. Apparently, such attempts were generally as unsuccessful in England as in the United States. We both spoke of our frequent surprise at the immaturity of mind and personality of many of our applicants.

Book writing seemed to be a pretty constant activity for Professor Hamilton. He now showed me the page proofs of a new textbook of anatomy, incorporating the most up-to-date information, and written by Hamilton in collaboration with Boyd of Cambridge and Le Gros Clark of Oxford. I also had an opportunity to see the manner in which he had worked in preparing a large section for another collaborative book, *The Physiology of Reproduction,* edited by Marshall.

"Perhaps you would like to see our museum first and then the laboratories," Doctor Hamilton said. We followed him into a large room with numerous specimens. The objects of interest here were by no means confined to the subject of human anatomy. The structure of other creatures has always been of great value for comparative studies with the human body, and details in other forms have often helped to elucidate and explain the anatomical make-up of man.

This museum contained an especially fine collection of casts of the respiratory tree and the lungs of many animals. Such casts are made by removing the parts in question from the animals, filling the windpipe and its branches, down to their finest ramifications in the lungs, with some suitable material such as a plastic or a metal of low melting point, and then removing the tissue, which has served as a mold, by treatment with a weak acid or by other means. Here we saw such casts made from the lion, tiger, seal and many other species. A point of general interest was the relatively great width of the trachea in carnivorous, as contrasted with herbivorous, animals.

We went on into the gross anatomy laboratory, where the dissection of the body is carried out. No actual work was in progress at this time, and the dozen or so tables were unoccupied. We spoke, as anatomists very often will, of the problem of the supply of bodies for dissection. While we have come a long way from the days of the bodysnatcher and of angry mobs threatening the medical schools, the number of specimens for dissection often is small. "We have had good fortune recently with the willing of bodies to our school," said the professor. "Only a short time ago, a member of the nobility (and he mentioned the name of a prominent English gentleman) willed his body to us. After all, it is only a kind of delayed burial."

We went into the laboratory of histology. Here this subject, the microscopic study of the tissues, was a part of the department of anatomy, but in many English schools it is found in the department of physiology. Conspicuous on the walls were photomicrographs from the recent work of our Canadian friend, Murray Barr, showing the sex chromatin which he had discovered as being visible in the female nerve cells and other cells of the body and which would thus allow one to distinguish the sex of an animal or person by examining a minute bit of tissue, a method later to find practical application. Here also were specimens of the placentas of various animals, deer, cows and others. We learned that Doctor R. J. Harrison, an expert in this field whom we had met only a short time before, had worked with Professor Hamilton a few years earlier.

Before our departure, Doctor Hamilton invited us to come, with our six-year old daughter, to have tea at his home in the suburb of Moor Park on the following Sunday.

* * *

That Sunday morning we had attended a service at Westminster Abbey. On previous visits I had been impressed at how really crowded with the illustrious dead this venerable structure is. On this pleasant Sunday morning, it was thronged with the living, as well.

After the service, we had gone for a boat ride on the Thames, from Westminster Bridge to the Tower, taking advantage of the unusual weather. Such a ride is a short review of many of the monuments of London, past and present, and seems almost to include an excursion in that fourth dimension of time which seems so much more important for human kind than for the other members of creation.

We ate a light lunch, rested an hour or so in our quarters on Half-Moon Street, and then set out for the Hamiltons' home.

It was a long ride, first by tube, then by regular train, but the route was an interesting one, passing from the heart of the metropolis out into the quiet suburbs.

At the station, Sandy Lodge and Moor Park, we were met by Hamilton, who drove us the short distance to his home. The house was a beautiful and stately old edifice. In the spacious living room, Mrs. Hamilton greeted us and we met the children, Peter and Ian, the two older boys, who were twins, and a daughter. Peter, a boy about ten, presented our daughter with a little ceramic horse of his own making.

We were shown the formal gardens behind the house and then came back to the living room where tea was served. As we were talking, it occurred to me to make a remark sup-

FIGURE 16   Coat of arms of the City of London, emblazoned on a brass
dinner-call.

posing that this peaceful area was well removed from the
terrible air blitz against London.

"Well, no, not really," said Doctor Hamilton. "We seemed to
be on the route of the Jerries on a good many occasions. Every
family around here had its own shelter somewhere near the
house, and when the sirens screamed we hit out for it." It
wasn't so much that the Germans thought these suburbs a
worthwhile or strategic target, but with the numbers of planes
coming over, and the roaring response of the Royal Air Force,
there were often some enemy airmen, thwarted in their major
objectives, who would drop their bombs at hazard. Of course
there were the dogfights high in the sky which might end in one

or more planes making a fiery plunge into the residential areas below.

Sitting here with this lovely English family, it was indeed hard to visualize the conditions of which we were talking and still harder to realize that many thousands of similar families had gone through those months and years of terror from the air. Yes, it was hard in many ways; and yet there was a feeling that the fiber of such families was just the stuff to weather such terror. Curiously, the humorous lines of Gilbert and Sullivan came to my mind.

> He is an Englishman!
> For he himself has said it,
> And it's greatly to his credit,
> That he is an Englishman.

Two of the children had gone out for some recreation over at the Merchant Taylors' College. Mrs. Hamilton was going to drive over to pick them up and bring them home, and her husband asked us if we would care to walk over with him. The day was still fair, and the three of us were very glad to stretch our legs. It gave us a chance for a closer look at the village and the delightful countryside. About a mile away, we came to the Merchant Taylors' College, a boys' school founded originally by the London Guild of Taylors for the education of their own sons but which had since come to include persons of other callings.

Just as we reached the school, a fine drizzle which had begun during the walk became a real downpour, and we took shelter under the eaves. In a few moments Mrs. Hamilton drove up with the children, and although it made pretty close quarters, we all got into the car. In spite of the rain, we decided to drive back by another route. The Hamiltons wished to show us the golf club nearby. Indeed, it turned out to be well worth seeing, for it was an ancient building erected as a countryhouse by Henry VIII and lived in for some time by Anne Boleyn. Later, it had been the home of nobility, a part of the estate of the Duke of Eberly. The turreted building was partly surrounded by huge oaks of as great or greater antiquity than itself, and tall ferns covered the grounds about it. Beyond, the rolling green, a modern golf course spread away into the distance.

We would have liked to wander a bit more, but with the late afternoon change in the weather, the fireplace back in the Hamilton livingroom was a welcome refuge. Before we left, our host mentioned to us that on the return trip we would be able to see from the train the extensive tract of land where the new buildings of the Charing Cross Hospital and of its medical school would be built within the next few years. This would be actually the first of the great medical institutions of London to leave the crowded central portion of the city and to seek breathing space farther out. It was a stimulating and exciting prospect, and it was easy to see the enthusiasm which Hamilton felt for it.

From the train we did see the site of the new Charing Cross institution. But we did not know, nor did Doctor Hamilton, professor of anatomy, know, that before the building was completed, he would have been named dean of the medical school and the chief guide of its future destiny.

Chapter 9

"THE PROPER STUDY OF MANKIND"

A Visit to Professor R. A. M. Bergman,
Chief Anthropologist at the
Royal Tropical Institute in Amsterdam

WE TOOK off from the London airport in the morning and winged toward Amsterdam, the largest city of the Netherlands. It was our first journey to Holland, and we were looking forward to a stay of a month there. During part of that time we would be attending the International Congress of Cell Biology in the historic city of Leyden and for the rest would be visiting the biological and medical laboratories in Amsterdam, Gröningen and Utrecht.

Best of all, we already had a friend in the Netherlands. It had been several years before that I had met Professor R. A. M. Bergman while we both were attending an international meeting in St. Louis, Missouri. At that time he had been back in the Netherlands for three years, having returned from a long career of teaching, research and medical practice in the East Indies.

The St. Louis meeting was the Second Congress of the International Gerontological Association, an organization dealing with problems of aging and the aged. Professor Bergman had published recently a paper entitled "Who is Old? Death Rate in a Japanese Concentration Camp as a Criterion of Age." Dominant in the camp, where Bergman himself was interned, assisting his fellow prisoners as well as he could, was the impression that older persons paid an unproportionately high toll. One would say, for example "I still have a chance, I am not yet

FIGURE 17 R. A. M. Bergman.

fifty," while another would say, "I have not much chance left, I am fifty already." Doctor Bergman, by an analysis of death among the over ten thousand internees, had verified the importance of the age factor and shown that after the age of thirty-five the death rate rose suddenly and continued to do so for the duration of the internment. He had pointed out, however, that previous way of life made a great difference in chances of survival.

The premature aging of the prisoners had been described in Doctor Bergman's writing, and he had remarked that much of it was a reversible process, for, since liberation, many had regained physical ability and mental fitness to an astonishing degree, althought they remained more grey and wrinkled than normal for their real age.

Professor Bergman had a sturdy Dutch frame, with no sign of impairment of his vigorous health from his years in the Tropics and his internment by the Japanese. His intellectual features were adorned by a small beard which seemed quite in place. He spoke English with hardly a trace of an accent, and as we had talked in the lobby of the hotel in St. Louis, I was much stimulated by his conversation, both through the attraction of his personality and knowledge and through the fact that I was in the company of a man with a background almost completely different from that of any other of my scientific acquaintances. At the time, there was a possibility of my going to Bangkok as a visiting professor, and therefore I was particularly interested in his description of life for Europeans or Americans in the Far East.

When we had parted, Professor Bergman had given me a cordial invitation to visit his laboratory when or if we ever should be in Amsterdam.

He recently had been appointed professor of anthropology of the faculty of medicine at the University of Amsterdam. Anthropology, the study of mankind, is a field of tremendous breadth, including the comparison of the physical traits of the races of men, living and extinct, and also the social and cultural attributes at all levels from savagery to the highest civilization. Professor Bergman was interested more in physical traits and approached closely my own field of anatomy, which concerns the structure of man, but deals with the make-up of the body in general, rather than with comparative or racial studies.

While we had travelled in Europe once before and had been in France, Switzerland, Italy and England on that previous visit, this was our first trip by air from one European city to another. We had been impressed by the great extent of the London International Airport and by the cosmopolitan atmosphere of its offices and waiting rooms. In the brief time before our own KLM flight was announced over the public address system, we heard planes announced for Düsseldorf, Cairo, and Bombay and a passenger for Istanbul being paged.

Now we were flying in a gray English sky, with little to see below us. Nancy and little Nancy, our daughter, were in one seat, while I was in another with a young man, whom I soon learned was a Japanese. The stewardess came by and asked if we would care for a snack. I accepted, but my seatmate was not responding too well to the roughness of the air, and I was glad that he had refused when I found the snack to consist of a *sausage* sandwich and broth.

We left behind the cliffs of the English coast, and now below us were the myriad white caps of the North Sea. In what seemed a very short time, we saw a long, wide beach and beyond it a land but little higher above the sea. We circled and landed smoothly at the airport of Amsterdam. At the entrance to the airport building a mat with "Holland Welcomes You!" in Engglish, greeted us. Inside, another rather pleasant experience was waiting, for a Dutch official told us that we had by mistake been overcharged for our baggage at the London office of KLM, and we very promptly received a refund. "It will pay your taxi fare!" he said in good English, smiling with a sympathetic pleasure.

A rather long ride by taxi brought us to the heart of Amsterdam and our hotel, the Victoria. That afternoon I made my first call on a Dutch telephone and had the great pleasure of hearing Professor Bergman's voice and being told that I might call at his laboratory the following day to discuss our arrangements in Amsterdam and our plans for the stay in Holland. We did little until evening, although then we did venture out to explore a part of the broad main street of Amsterdam, the Damrak. We enjoyed delicious sandwiches and well-made coffee at a little restaurant, the Narco, and walked as far as De Biejenkorf (The Beehive), a huge department store. The street and store fronts were gaily decorated, but we did not learn why until the next day.

In the morning after a continental breakfast of rolls and coffee, which reminded us that we had left England behind, we decided that we all three would go out to the neighborhood of the Institute but that for this initial visit, I would leave the two Nancys and would go alone to Doctor Bergman's laboratory.

When we are able to spend more than a few days in any city abroad, we make it a point to use the local transportation rather than taxis, not only for economy but also because it is a much better way to come to know the streets and squares *and* the people of a city. It was a matter of only a few moments' inquiry to learn that the Koninklijk Instituut voor den Tropen could be reached very easily by a number 9 tram. We walked a block to the tramstop in front of the great Central Station. Here we could

FIGURE 18 A tile from an old Dutch house (eighteenth century) destroyed in the Nazi bombings.

catch glimpses of the extensive water front of Amsterdam. The city is situated where the Amstel flows into the Y (pronounced as *i*), or Ijselmeer, an arm of the Zuiderzee, the inland sea of the Netherlands, called the South Sea in contrast to the North Sea or outer sea.

Our tram ride took us along busy modern streets but gave us also our first view of the amazing system of canals or *grachten* which penetrates to every part of the metropolis. Steep stone banks border the calm surfaces of these waterways. With the very slight elevation at which Amsterdam lies, the construction of the canals was a most logical undertaking. The water in them is generally only three to three and a half feet deep and is renewed constantly from an arm of the North Sea Canal. Many of the *grachten* are flanked by avenues of stately elms and present a majestic and tranquil appearance. Incidentally, all of the buildings have had to be constructed on foundations of piles, up to sixty feet in length, driven down through the overlying mud and into the firmer sand of the deeper levels. The learned Erasums of Rotterdam was speaking jestingly of his sister community when he said: "I know a city whose inhabitants dwell on the tops of trees like rooks."

We now had left the business section well behind, and we alighted near the beautiful Singelgracht on Linnaeusstraat. Our first view of the Institute was somewhat of a surprise, for we hardly had expected the massive, castlelike building which we saw before us. Its great bulk was lightened by rounded towers and graceful spires, while trees and shrubbery softened the harshness of its dark walls. We located a small but pleasant coffee shop which had a hospitable proprietor and was decked with fresh flowers. Here the ladies could await me. I crossed the avenue and entered the hallway. A member of the staff of the museum took me to the door of Professor Bergman's laboratory; his secretary, an alert young woman, greeted me. "Please come in and have a chair," she said. "The professor will be here soon."

The room was a large one, a combination of laboratory and study. A long table in the center held apparatus and specimens of various types. Toward one end of the room was Bergman's desk, while that of his secretary was to one side. Wide windows gave a view of a wooded park behind the Institute. Bookcases along the wall held hundreds of volumes on anthropological topics, in English and in most of the continental languages.

Doctor Bergman arrived very soon. He treated me with cordial affection and expressed great pleasure that we were now to be in the Netherlands for some time. "First," he said, "you will want a home." We sat down at his desk, and he began to give me names of some persons and places for apartment hunting. It was not a simple thing, to find a temporary place, for living space was still at a premium in Holland. Coupled with the destruction of the war and the delay in new building which it had caused was the influx of Dutch families returning from the East Indies, of which, indeed, my friend's family was one. Among other names, he gave me that of Mr. Jan Nikerk, Director of Tourism for the Netherlands and very fortunately for us, a good friend of Doctor Bergman. On this visit I stayed a short time only, as my friend realized our wish to settle ourselves as true "Amsterdamers." Returning to the little coffee shop, I found that the ladies had been having a pleasant time during my wait. A tape-recorded musical program was in full swing, and my daughter was dancing about to its melody. Nancy told me that the proprietor had informed her that the shop was newly opened, and the many flowers were in honor of the occasion.

We decided to go directly to the office of Mr. Nikerk. We found him a very busy man in a busy office, but he met us with the greatest courtesy. Besides the addresses of several possible places for us to stay, he gave us three tickets to go aboard a ship next morning from which we would have a good view of the arrival of King Haakon of Norway, who was paying a state visit to the Netherlands. It was for this royal visit that the Damrak was so gaily decorated. One of the addresses which we received was that of Doctor Mathyi, a physician who owned a home at 78 Nicolas Maesstraat (a street named, like many another in Dutch cities, for a famous master of painting). Doctor Mathyi wished to rent several rooms, which included a balcony at the rear looking over trim Dutch gardens. The place was modest, but really ideal for us, and we settled there that same afternoon.

Doctor Bergman had invited me to come to the Institute again as soon as would be convenient, and, as I was very eager to learn more of the work carried out in that important center and in particular to know more of the methods of research and of the scientific philosophy of my friend, it was only a few days later that I paid him a second visit, this time accompanied by Nancy. This time he was already in his laboratory and with him were two young ladies. He introduced us to them. One was his niece, the other, a friend of hers, from Antwerp. It was very interesting to us to learn that the language of Antwerp is Flemish, a descendant, as it were, of the Dutch language and differing not very greatly from it. The separation actually is the result of the historical fact of the breaking away of the northern provinces from Spanish rule while the southern ones remained Spanish and Catholic.

Doctor Bergman was just beginning to demonstrate a diopto-graph to the girls, and we joined them as spectators. This is an ingenious piece of apparatus used in craniometry, the measurement of the skull, or more properly, of the brain-containing portion of the skull, the cranium. The data obtained by use of this instrument give the proportions of the skull and the angles between lines drawn connecting certain definite landmarks on it. From such data the races of mankind can be compared, and modern man can be studied in relation to the fossil remains of prehistoric man. Among the more simple classifications of skulls is that made by means of the cephalic index (ratio of cranial width to cranial length, i.e., of side-to-side measurement with front-to-rear measurements). Thus the Negro, with an index of 70, is dolichocephalic, the European, with one of 80, is mesaticephalic and the Samoyed, a Siberian tribesman, with one of 85, is brachycephalic. Doctor Bergman had completed his demonstration of the dioptograph. "Come along," he said. "Let me show you some of our museum specimens."

We left the laboratory and began a journey which was to us

very much like a safari of exploration in the vast halls of the museum, with our friend as guide. Very few visitors were present at this time of the day, and the sensation was not unlike that of strolling through a metropolis in the very early morning when its broad avenues are almost deserted. Only here the "shop windows" were the impressive museum cases—windows which opened now on one strange and exotic scene, now on another. Here was a window into the hut of the tribesmen of New Guinea. Prominently displayed was a decorated skull. It was not, explained Doctor Bergman, a trophy of some raid upon an enemy tribe. On the contrary, it was the deeply revered skull of the deceased head of the household—an object of respect and even affection, which remains for months in the "family circle." This is an example of the custom of skull veneration—a strange tradition and, to us of the civilized world, one even of pathos when we consider the way in which it expresses the reluctance of the living to acknowledge that the dead have truly departed.

We moved on and paused to look through another window. Here we were viewing a model of a pyramid or, perhaps better, a terraced mountain. As our friend spoke to us, it seemed to swell to its true dimensions while its many thousands of carved figures assumed a vivid and breathtaking reality, for this was the *Boro Budur*, the "Mountain of Buddha." This holy structure lies on the central plain of Java. It is a hill which was transformed into a stupendous temple by the labors of countless worshippers some two centuries before William the Conqueror came to England. Over 500 feet on each side of its square base, the giant structure rises in tiers, with a majestic stairway on each face passing upward beneath the grim faces of monsters. Everywhere are statues and rich carvings in relief. On the upper tiers, in a series of deep niches, are over 400 colossal figures of the Buddha. The innumerable reliefs portray scenes from the life of the Enlightened One, who lived five centuries before Christ, and from the history and literature of Indian civilization. Saints, warriors, elephants and a multitude of other forms cover every wall.

Far up, on the three uppermost tiers, rise small pinnacled domes, each one walled by a lattice of stonework. Within each may be dimly seen a figure of a seated Buddha. But at the very summit the dome is plain, as if human art had been left behind. Here was the shrine, the Holy of Holies. What did it contain? "We do not know what sacred objects crowned this tremendous monument," said Doctor Bergman, "but many say that it was the ashes of Gautama Buddha himself!" How can the history of such a work as the *Boro Budur* have been lost in oblivion? As in many another case, it is largely the story of conquest— in Java, the triumph of an invading Islam over the more ancient civilizations of India and the Indies.

We left the spacious halls and entered a small but exquisitely arranged exhibit room—the Hall of Islam. Here were reproduced in the minutest detail scenes from the life and religious customs of the Moslems. Models of palaces and mosques showed the lightness and beauty of the Mohammedan architecture, with its slender columns and cloudlike domes—all devoid of figures, either of human beings or animals—for the Moslems are iconoclasts, not only in the destruction of idols of the other religions but in the severe prohibition of the use of imitations of living beings in their work. In one corner we could actually peer into the interior of a mosque where life-sized figures were engaged in worship.

On the far wall of the room was a large map of Islam—the Mohammedan world of some 235 million souls—stretching from the Atlas Mountains at the Straits of Gibraltar across the countries of North Africa and the Middle East through Persia, Afghanistan, a large portion of India, and on to embrace wide areas of the East Indies. To our western minds, such a map is apt to bring forth pictures of the warriors of the Prophet in bloody conflict and of the conquest and subjugation of one nation after another. Yet *Islam* itself means a surrender—a yielding to Allah and his will, and not all of the conquests by Mohammedanism have been by the sword alone.

We left the Hall of Islam and passed many other windows, opening to Sumatra, to Bali, to Surinam and to Curaçao, reminders also of how widespread have been the influence and activities of the Dutch. Particularly fascinating were scenes of the jungles of the Tropics both of the East and West, for each type of plant and animal life was arranged in so natural a manner that one almost could feel the hot moist atmosphere among the trees and vines and look expectantly for a movement by the coiled serpent, the glittering beetle or the iridescent butterflies.

We descended now to the main floor and in the largest of the halls viewed magnificent exhibits from the East Indies and the islands of the South Pacific. The recurring figures of the snake made me recall the prominence of the feathered serpent in Mexico and in the cities of the Mayas, and I mentioned to Doctor Bergman a book which I had read years before, *The Children of the Serpent,* a volume rich in descriptions of the beliefs and customs of widely scattered primitive peoples. In it the author drew conclusions as to a probable common origin of such peoples and of the Cult of the Serpent. "It is very curious," said Doctor Bergman. "As you probably know, there are two schools with divergent ideas on this subject." I was pleased to see that, learned as he was in these matters, he was not ready to scoff at ideas which among some anthropologists would be considered as too radical for consideration.

We returned now to the laboratory and in a little discussion learned further details about the Institute and the work of our host. Until recent years the name had been "Institute of the Indies," for Indonesia, the vast collection of some 30,000 islands, with a population of 80,000,000 persons, had been to the Netherlands what India was to England. We were to hear more later, both from Doctor Bergman and from others, about the profound effect which the loss of this great territory was having upon the mother country and upon individual Dutchmen.

It was time for us to depart. Doctor Bergman asked me how he might be of aid in some of my other visits in Amsterdam and other cities of the Netherlands, and I gave him the names of several of the faculty members at the University and of other investigators whom I hoped to meet, in order that he might make an initial telephone call. With assurance that we would meet soon again, we took our leave.

During the next few weeks I was in and out of Amsterdam a good deal, visiting Utrecht, Gröningen, Leiden, the Hague and other cities of the Netherlands, usually with an introduction through Doctor Bergman or with valuable information which he had given me on the important things to see and scientists to meet. However, I was in the city enough of the time for several very pleasant opportunities for our families to be together and for me to learn more of Professor Bergman's history and background. His life had not been an easy one, for it had been affected early by personal and family problems, the conflicts of the European nations and later by the overrunning of Indonesia by the Japanese.

His grandfather and great-grandfather had been army officers, and his father might have followed in their steps had it not been for a congenital heart condition. When the boy Bergman was only three years old, his mother died in childbirth when a sister was born. Only a short time after this sad occurence, his father, who had originally been well-to-do, lost most of his money, and his life never was an easy one after that. The education of his two children became his single remaining aim in life. He impressed upon his son the high esteem in which he held scientific study and the fact that the boy's mother had felt this way also. When young Bergman was five years old, the family moved to Belgium. There, as he was growing up, he was surrounded by the conflict, often a bitter one, between the leaders of the Flemish part of the population and the protagonists of the French language and culture. Then, when he was only fifteen years old, came the First World War. Too young to be called to service, he still was old enough to feel the horror and futility of the holocaust.

Shortly after young Bergman had passed his first university examination, and after his sister had completed fitting herself for a career in teaching, their father died. His death left his son with a feeling of bereavement and emptiness and, in spite of his love of study, he left the university and entered a business office. Fortunately, his sister's advice and his own inclination led him to return to his education within a year. Bergman's school was the University of Utrecht. Here he was fortunate in finding on the faculty a number of outstanding scientific workers. There was the professor of physiology, Doctor Zwaardemaker, the histologist, Boeke, and, among the clinical teachers, the world-renowned neurologist, Winkler. After passing the candidate's examination, Bergman remained at Utrecht as assistant in histology and embryology for three years. He had become attached to Heringa, who now was appointed professor of histology at the University of Amsterdam. Bergman went with him, again as assistant in this field. He was able to receive, a year later, his degree of Doctor of Medicine for work which he had done at Utrecht. This was in 1927.

Meanwhile, he had married. Both his wife and he were of an adventurous turn of mind, and neither feared the difficulties of new lands and encounters with little-known peoples and surroundings. To such persons in Holland, the great land of Indonesia, with its millions of inhabitants of varied races and religions, and a multitude of strange animals and plants, beckoned as a symbol of romance and opportunity, where useful, absorbing and often profitable careers were to be had. Doctor Bergman was to serve as lecturer at the medical school in Djakarta. He planned to bring to this school the techniques of tissue culture which he had studied in Dahlem (Berlin) under Fischer and in Turin under Levi, and of micromanipulation, or surgery under the microscope, which he had studied in Holland under Péterfi and Schouten.

But the plans for research on cells met with sad frustrations, for both he and Mrs. Bergman contracted severe malaria. Then the great depression set in, and although we may at times forget the fact, it was felt over almost the whole world. The budget of the University had to be heavily curtailed.

Bergman was not one to be easily discouraged. As he said to me, "Really, there was too much to do to grumble for very long about the things which we could not do!" He turned from his interest in microscopic research to the fascinating problems of race and constitution, to studies on the characterization of the peoples of Indonesia by body form and skeletal features.

Indeed, it was this circumstance which led him into the study of mankind, in which he was to gain such eminence as to receive many years later the highest appointment in anthropology which the Dutch government could give, the post which he now held. During this time also the problems of comparative anatomy and of evolution began to occupy his attention.

When, in 1932, the head of the department of anatomy went on furlough, Bergman took this post for a year. A similar acting headship, this time at the medical school in Surabaia in the eastern part of Java, occupied the next year. Then came an opportunity for the Bergmans to return to Holland for two years, an apportunity which was welcomed not so much from homesickness as from the fine contacts with departments in the universities where Bergman could discuss the studies in anthropology and comparative anatomy which he had made already and which he planned for the future.

Soon after his return to Indonesia, he had the choice of a position in Djakarta, the capital, or in Surubaia. He chose the latter. However, because of the rather low and not-too-healthful situation of Surubaia, it was decided that Mrs. Bergman and the children would live in Malang, in the hills, and that Doctor Bergman would spend the week ends there.

These were fruitful years in teaching and research. Surely, Holland was repaying much to Indonesia in sending such professors as Bergman to improve the medical training of her native doctors! But the conflicts of nations were soon to influence the life of Bergman again. The armies of imperial Japan were overrunning vast territories of the Far East, and now they struck at the Netherlands' East Indies. With the mother country already under German occupation there was little hope in resistance by the Dutch or by the Indonesians. The Bergman family was among the thousands placed in internment camps, Bergman in one camp and his wife and children in another, many miles away.

"These years were indeed miserable," said Bergman, "but also, I must say, extremely instructive. Whereas it had seemed more profitable to me earlier to study human morphology, it now seemed better to study human behavior. I was allowed to practice medicine and thus to aid the fellow internees in my camp. I have felt that my observations and laboratory studies during that time taught me many things which I would not have learned under more normal conditions." Bergman spoke little of the way in which he was treated by his Japanese captors. He did say "Working in a more or less constant expectation of death is a curious experience."

Yet during this time in the Kesilir concentration camp in East Java, Bergman carried out interesting studies on the blood cells of the native snakes, using a resourceful method to make this possible. Every morning a tour of the camp was made to collect blood samples from those persons who showed any rise in temperature. Only if parasites were found in the blood smears could the patient be given any of the very limited supply of quinine. Very limited also was the supply of special stain for the blood. This stain was freshly diluted for use with the human blood, and coloring was carried out for a long period in highly diluted dye. Even then, the used stain from which the slides of human blood had been removed was not thrown away, but it was this stain which was used to color the blood of various species of Javanese snakes. In this way, Bergman made studies, published after the war, on blood from forty-two snakes of twelve different species. A very interesting fact to me was that Dr. Bergman discovered malarial parasites in the blood of six of the forty-two snakes! I had not known that these scaly reptiles even were bitten by mosquitoes!

In 1945 the allied planes roared over the islands, and troops by thousands landed to force the Japanese from their strongholds. Freed, Bergman found his wife and children—all but the youngest, ill—in a concentration camp at Semarang. There was many a tale to tell, and many a quiet tear to shed in gratefulness at the reunion. The greatest hardship at Semarang had been hunger. Perhaps starvation is a better word. The meager ration of the prisoners barely held body and soul together. The greatest torment, Mrs. Bergman said, was for the famine-stricken prisoners to catch the odors of food cooking from the camp of

the Japanese. Then crying and wailing and screaming would re-
sound in the prisoners' compound. With courageous foresight,
the mother of the Bergman children would hold back a little
portion of the scant ration of rice which they had been given
and just at this time would give the hoarded food to them.

Reunion for the Bergmans did not mean immediate rescue
from danger. Carrying his family through Java, Bergman found
that they were the first white people travelling by ambulance
car. Their road lay through insurgent territory, for already the
anti-colonial sentiment was being fanned into flame. Fortunately,
the people themselves were friendly enough, and they met with
no violence.

As we sat with Professor and Mrs. Bergman in a little Indonesian restaurant on one of the main thoroughfares of Amsterdam, it seemed a far cry indeed from hardship and starvation.
They were introducing us to the *Ricetafel,* a special feature of
culinary art of Java and neighboring islands. A great variety
of individual items made up the meal, nearly every one a surprise to us. There were fried bananas, savory meat on skewers,
coconut and great mounds of rice. Here, too, we first ate some
of the very palatable and nutritious dishes made from the protein of the soya bean.

While we were in Amsterdam, the Bergmans were living in
a small apartment. They were on a waiting list for a house, but
conditions were still crowded in postwar Holland. Yet even the
small apartment had become a comfortable and indeed a fascinating home. The furniture was attractively old-fashioned,
while Indonesian paintings enlivened the walls. A friendly over-
grown dog of wolflike appearance named Raksha (after the
mother wolf or "demon" of Kipling's *Jungle Book*) shared the
apartment with the Bergmans. In Bergman's study were some
of the most beautiful and curious oriental figures which we
had ever seen, some from the Indies, some from the mainland
of Asia.

It was easy to see when visiting in the little apartment that the
Bergmans were a happy family—happy in being together. And it
was little wonder, because, even after the liberation from Java,

Bergman had found it necessary to be away from his wife and children for several years; while he sent them back to the Netherlands, he remained in Melbourne as head of medical services for the Dutch evacuees until 1947. After that he had spent two years as head of the municipal medical service in Djakarta, where he was a liaison agent between the Indonesian republicans and the Dutch, an important and sensitive post. His return to the Netherlands was to a country greatly altered by war and the world-shaking postwar happenings. It must have been a pleasant experience to enter the Department of Anthropology at the Royal Tropical Institute and to be able again to think the long, long thoughts of the man of science.

But it is to no monastic quiet that Doctor Bergman has returned. There is here an activity of great importance—an activity greatly disrupted by the loss of the Dutch East Indies and demanding a new organization. Its rebuilding is an important challenge in the world picture of anthropology, the "Proper Study of Mankind."

In a time in which man has so expanded his control over the physical universe, from the interior of the atom to the vastnesses of outer space, the study of his own nature remains an enormous task, one upon which may depend his very existence. It is a task which must go forward, and if we should feel discouraged at times at the little progress made thus far, we may recall the words of Lao Tze, words with which Professor Bergman closed his address on the occasion of his inauguration as professor of anthropology at the University of Amsterdam:

> A journey of a thousand miles began with a single step.

Chapter 10

STATESMAN OF SCIENCE
A Visit to Professor Edmund Vincent Cowdry

FORTUNATELY, the opportunity for knowing Edmund Vincent Cowdry has come to me not simply through a visit to his laboratory, important as that first visit was, but through a longer stay, one of six months, in his department at Washington University. Then, too, there have been numerous more casual meetings in widely separated locations in many parts of the world.

It was very early in my scientific career that the name Cowdry became known to me. Indeed, anyone becoming interested in the study of cells soon found that the two major works of reference in this field had been edited by him. These works were *General Cytology*, a single weighty tome, the individual chapters of which had been written by different authors and *Special Cytology*, a three-volume work, also of the multiple-authored type. Both of them had been fascinating to me. The first seemed to open the doors to the past history of the subject and to the labors of the earlier cytologists, Fleming, Boveri, Wilson and others who were advancing into a new world of knowledge. By the exacting study of the eggs of sea urchins and starfish, by the observation of tissues of invertebrates and of amphibians, these men had begun to unravel some of the profound secrets of life. The second work, with its separation into sections dealing with the cellular make-up of each individual organ of the body, was impressive in showing the immense amount of detail of structure to be learned and also the need for more study in each case in order to elucidate the relation between structure and function.

FIGURE 19   Edmund Vincent Cowdry.

In sending out the reprints of my first several scientific papers, I included Doctor Cowdry on the small mailing list, hardly expecting more than a purely formal acknowledgment of their receipt by his secretary. It was with surprise, then, that I opened the acknowledgment from his office to find not only a personal letter from Doctor Cowdry but also one which displayed the keenest interest in and understanding of the problem on which I had been working: the changes with age in the nerve cells of the brain.

During the next several years of my research, an occasional communication from Cowdry was a source of very real encouragement. At the time, I was teaching, carrying a part-time medical curriculum which made considerable demands on time and receiving a stipend which even by near-depression standards, was barely adequate for existence for a young married couple. Under these circumstances the knowledge that so distinguished a scientist as Cowdry felt that my research efforts were worthwhile meant a great deal to me.

It was only a short time after I had obtained an instructorship in Dallas, Texas, with a somewhat increased income, that an opportunity arose to visit Doctor Cowdry. We were making a trip north which would take us through St. Louis. There was at the time also a very good reason to seek the advice of such an organizer and leader as Cowdry, for the excitement of new plans was in the air at our medical school. There was much talk of an expansion of research and an addition of laboratory space. For a long time I had cherished a hope that an Institute of Gerontology, a suite of laboratories, staffed with adequate scientific and technical personnel, might be set up. The plans which I had drawn I now would carry to Doctor Cowdry. In this field, the study of aging, his name already was one of the greatest importance. Under his editorship, the first group effort at a broad scientific treatment of the subject had been undertaken. Publication of Cowdry's *Problems of Aging* marked the beginning of a great surge of effort in gerontology.

We stopped in a downtown hotel in St. Louis. The next morning I set out for Washington University.

The school of medicine, far removed from the main campus of the University, lies just across the street from massive Barnes Hospital. Doctor Cowdry's office was on the second floor and, avoiding the large, old self-operated elevator, which I was to use so many times in the future, I walked up. The secretary, a young lady of somewhat overaverage weight and with a very impressive air of efficiency, even bustle, greeted me with some familiarity, for correspondence often gives a sense of acquaintanceship. From her smaller office, she led me into that of Cowdry. As he rose to greet me, I could not help thinking, even in that fraction of time, how well he lived up to my expectations. His was a trim but sturdy figure, fit for a man of such physical as well as intellectual activity. His countenance was a striking one, by its animation and its combination of a type of determined firmness blended somehow with a quiet good humor which was almost immediately felt in his presence. This blend of two of the best elements which a man may have has been an attribute of his through all of the years since, and through many times of real trial and stress, when physical illnesses or political cares might well have caused the determination to waver or the good humor to turn to bitterness. We sat and talked for the better part of an hour. Doctor Cowdry expressed a warm interest in my own scientific history, which really was a rather brief one at that time. In turn, I had the opportunity to learn at first hand of some of the episodes in his own career, which had been one not only filled with accomplishment but also one which could be described as truly adventurous and colorful.

Born in MacLeod, Canada, on July 18, 1888, Cowdry had gravitated toward science at an early age. "It was clearly my father who led me into the domain of science," he has said. "Although he was by profession a banker, he was also a naturalist in the whole and best sense of the word. He was familiar with rocks, flowers and animals and we often observed them together and, with his help and encouragement, I came to learn how to use a microscope." After graduation from the University of Toronto, Edmund had gone to the University of Chicago for graduate work. Here he came under the guidance and inspiration of a man who has had a far-reaching influence—Professor Robert R. Bensley. It was at this time that Bensley was beginning to open up an entire new field, one dealing particularly with the *chemical* attributes of cells and tissues, and the atmosphere in his laboratory was a very stimulating one. During his graduate work, Cowdry served also as assistant and then as associate in anatomy.

In 1913, with a Ph.D. to his credit, Cowdry went as associate in anatomy to another department of anatomy with a highly stimulating atmosphere—that of the Johns Hopkins University. This was the department of Franklin Payne Mall, one of the greatest anatomists, of Florence R. Sabin, the able student of the blood cells and blood-forming tissues and of George Wash-

ington Corner, then a young assistant in the anatomical laboratory and later to become director of the Carnegie Institute
of Embryology.

Four years were spent at Johns Hopkins, and then came an
opportunity for service in a far-off, and to many, mysterious
part of the world—China! The Rockefeller Foundation, fountain
of scientific activity on New York's East River, was sponsoring
the Peking Union Medical College in China. Cowdry was invited to go to Peking as the professor of anatomy. This phase
of his career made a profound impression upon his future work
and, I believe, on his attitude toward persons and affairs. In
later years, his graduate laboratories at Washington University
were liberally sprinkled with eager young scientists from China,
and in his great work of organizing international meetings it
has seemed most natural for him always to think in the broadest
and most cosmopolitan of terms.

It was time now for Cowdry to leave his medical school office. "Just now," he said, "I have not one position, but two. For
I spend a part of each day serving as director of research for
the Barnard Free Skin and Cancer Hospital." I was ready to
excuse myself, but he cordially invited me to go along to his
other post. "We can return here later and see more of the
anatomy department," he said.

We drove several miles through the city to reach the Barnard
Hospital and Clinic. The first floor here was in the nature of an
outpatient department. Scores of patients, many of them from
the surrounding rural areas, were waiting for diagnosis or treatment. This was for me a unique institution, for only lesions of
the skin and probable precancerous or cancerous growths were
accepted as cases. The term precancerous here was of the
greatest significance. "There are several conditions of the skin,"
Doctor Cowdry told me, "which, while not frankly cancerous,
so often lead on into cancer, that the term 'precancerous' is
an appropriate one. In these lesions we feel that we may be able
to see and study the very beginning of cancer and learn what
changes in the cells make them become the malignant creatures
which destroy the body."

We took the elevator to an upper floor, devoted entirely to laboratories of research. Here I had a splendid opportunity to see Cowdry, the scientific administrator, the organizer and leader of research, in his own element. As we went from one laboratory to another, he greeted the investigators of his team, singly or in groups, with an easy familiarity and yet a quick attention to the work at hand. Here a doctor from Poland was concentrating on the microscopic appearance of tissue sections. There a young biochemist was engaged, with flasks and retorts, in a complicated chemical analysis. In the next laboratory, a group was concerned with spectroscopic studies. These research workers, led by Cowdry, were studying not only naturally arising cancer, but also were producing, in the skin of mice, actual but artificial cancers. These were brought about by repeated application of methylcholanthrene (isolated by Kenneway and Cook in London), a coal tar derivative, to the skin of the experimental animals. Like natural or spontaneous cancer, the tissue which arose from this treatment was malignant, grew and spread, and eventually destroyed the animal which was its host. It was the *early* stages in its development, however, which were offering to Cowdry and his research team excellent opportunities for the study of the first stages in the transformation of normal to malignant tissue.

We sat down at a laboratory bench and Cowdry pointed out beneath the microscope the scene of a cancer in birth. There, at the surface of the tissue, was the apparently normal epidermis, composed of thousands upon thousands of cells, overlying the fibrous connective tissue, or dermis, of the skin. In one area, however, where the methylcholanthrene had done its work, the epidermis had undergone a strange transformation, its cells appeared different, and masses of them were penetrating downward into the connective tissue and breaking away. Here was the invasion of the organism by newly formed cancer cells!

As we entered the next laboratory, Cowdry said to me, with a bit of obvious pride, "And here is how we separate the pure epidermis from other tissues." A number of specimens of mouse skin were undergoing a treatment by temperature change, simple in itself, but remarkably effective in lifting the outer-most, cellular layer of the skin cleanly away from the under-lying layer, the dermis.

"Since it is only in the epidermis," Doctor Cowdry was saying, "that the transformation from normal to cancerous cells occurs, we have tried to isolate this tissue for our studies—particularly for the chemical analyses, and our new method really is working well." Later I to realized more fully the im-portance of this method when I heard Cowdry and others of his group present the differences between normal and cancer tissue in great detail, in papers given at national meetings of the anatomists and of other scientific groups.

Cowdry now left me with one of the biochemists for an hour or so, while he attended to paperwork here, in his second office. We returned to the medical school for lunch and talked during and after it of the organization of laboratory work. I showed Doctor Cowdry the plans for work on aging which I had drawn up in a tentative way. He commended my thinking and at the same time offered several helpful suggestions as to details.

Cowdry's own initiation to the complexities of carefully organized research had come upon his return from China, when he had served for seven years at the Rockefeller Institute for Medical Research, at that time under the leadership of the famous bacteriologist, Simon Flexner.

In his first year at the Institute, Cowdry had begun a study of the nature of Rickettsia bodies in mammalian and insect tissue, a study which was eventually to take him from New York to the Dark Continent. Rickettsia bodies may seem far removed from ordinary life, but it is various types of these organisms which have caused disastrous epidemics of typhus fever, which bring about the spotted fever of our own Rocky Mountains and which afflicted the troops of World War I with trench fever. In each case the organisms are carried by an insect or arachnid and reach the human being through its bite. In the case of Rocky Mountain spotted fever, a particular species of tick is responsible; in the case of typhus fever and trench fever, body lice are the culprits.

With his excellent training in cytology, Cowdry was able to add much to the knowledge of these diseases. In October of 1924, Sir Arnold Theiler, Director of Veterinary Education and Research of the Union of South Africa, visited the Rockefeller Institute. Prominent in his mind at that time was the problem of a disease of cattle in South Africa, a condition known as heartwater, because of the accumulation of fluid about the heart in the afflicted animals. Sir Arnold suspected that the disease might be transmitted by ticks and might, indeed, be caused by a Rickettsia organism. Deeply impressed by what he saw of Cowdry's studies at the institute, he invited him to come to work in Africa.

Cowdry's attack on this problem was a good example of what a trained mind, an excellent knowledge of technical methods, and a sound theoretical basis can do toward solving a question in science. Within two months he had identified a Rickettsia type of organism in the diseased cattle. The minute organisms were demonstrated to be *inside* of the cells lining the blood vessels of the kidney, brain and other organs. The creatures were seen particularly well when the cattle were having a febrile reaction and while their blood was infective. Not only did Cowdry demonstrate these facts but he showed that the Rickettsia would appear within cells of the intestine of ticks which were allowed to feed on the blood of the cattle. Thus the ticks became long-term transmitters. The cycle was completed when Cowdry found, in hitherto healthy animals upon which these ticks were allowed to feed, the same Rickettsia organisms.

On this first trip to Africa, the young scientist came upon another disease condition of peculiar interest, his contact with which foreshadowed in a way his later work in cancer research. In a letter dated November 11, 1924, and addressed to Doctor Simon Flexner, he says: ". . . the pathological histology of the condition . . . I hope, however, may be interesting because it is so very unusual and stands on the borderline between an overgrowth and a true neoplasm." This was the condition of the lungs known as *jagsiekte* or the "driving sickness," because it

FIGURE 20   On the trail of disease-producing organisms in Africa. The scene shows Doctor Hideyo Noguchi near Accra, in an expedition for the study of the yellow fever virus.

would first show up in sheep who were being driven along and who thus were seen to be unable to stand exertion. It showed a remarkable new growth of tissue combined with evidences of inflammation.

Less than a week later a second letter from Cowdry to Flexner informed him that, at a dinner given jointly for members of the laboratory staff and of the medical faculty of the University of Witwatersrand, Sir Arnold had formally announced the discovery of the causative organism of heartwater fever.

Success thus had crowned Cowdry's efforts in South Africa. Nevertheless, that the path was not an entirely smooth one can be seen in an excerpt from a letter: ". . . the photographer here has worked faithfully trying to make photomicrographs, thus far without success." In spite of the restrained tone, one can imagine some of the frustration here of not being able to catch on film or plate the tiny microorganisms so beautifully demonstrated on Cowdry's slides.

One final excerpt from a letter, this one from Sir Arnold Theiler to Simon Flexner, seems worthy of record in showing the impression which Cowdry had made in this distant land. Sir Arnold says: "His keenness has been an inspiration to my assistants . . ."

The stay in Africa was cut short by increasingly alarming news of the ill health of Cowdry's father. Actually, his death came before his son had reached the United States.

He made a second trip to Africa, this time to Tunisia to study some of the organisms which invade the red blood corpuscles of animals. In Cowdry's own words, the object of this expedition was "to become thoroughly familiar with the dozen or more parasites of this kind in North Africa and to bring back material for study." Just when all the arrangements for the trip had been made, a telegram came to Flexner, as director of the Rockefeller Institute, from the Colonial Secretary, asking that Cowdry be sent to study certain diseases in Kenya Colony. But he already was committed to Tunis.

Among the interesting by-products of the Tunis study was a demonstration in a malaria type of protozoan, Plasmodium praecox, of the presence of both mitochondria and neutral red granules, showing the lack of identity of these two kinds of structures.

Cowdry's fascination with the organelles, or little organs of the cell, was shown in many of his studies during his years at the Rockefeller Institute. In fact, when he first arrived there, a considerable doubt existed in the minds of some scientists as to whether the mitochondria, tiny rod and threadlike bodies in the cytoplasm of the cell, might be actually microorganisms themselves, for they bear a rather striking superficial resemblance to many of the bacteria. For the work of deciding this question, there was no one better suited than Edmund V. Cowdry. A sort of prospective of his work is given in one of the Annual Scientific Reports to the Members of the Corporation of the Rockefeller Institute, dated October 20, 1922, which says: "The working out of this distinction by Doctor Cowdry should be final, as he is an acknowledged authority on mitochondrial elements." Cowdry already had been interested in the cell components for some years, and the stimulation of his interest while at Johns Hopkins had even led his father, Nathaniel Cowdry, banker, to carry out work and publish scientific papers after his retirement!

The work at the Rockefeller Institute did settle this important question of distinguishing bacteria and mitochondria. Cowdry and his colleagues devised various ingenious methods for this study. For instance, they studied mitochondria within living cells of the lymph, side by side with bacteria, under identical conditions, and they injected bacteria into just-removed pancreatic tissue and studied them along with the mitochondria of pancreatic cells. Different reactions to various fluids and stains were shown by these experiments, and a concept which well might have clouded the field of cytology for many years, the belief that mitochondria are bacterial cells, was quietly relegated to its place in the history of scientific error, where indeed it enjoys very distinguished company. With these and other contributions to the knowledge of the cell, it was not surprising that Cowdry was offered the position as professor of cytology at Washington University in 1928. At the time of my first visit to his laboratory, he had served in this post for over twelve years and already had been for several years director of research of the Barnard Hospital.

He took me now from his office to some of the research laboratories of the department of anatomy. Here were being developed the techniques and methods of approach of histochemistry, the identification and localization of specific chemical substances within the cells. One of the more interesting of these to me was that called microincineration (devised by Policard in Paris), by which the organic substance of cells in a thin section are literally consumed by heat, leaving the fine ash of inorganic substances which appears on a dark background as a brilliant skeleton, reproducing most of the features of the cell seen before the treatment. The color of the ash indicates the chemical nature, red for iron, blue for potassium and white for calcium and magnesium.

The graduate students and faculty research persons in Cowdry's department were by no means confined to studies on cancer. "Many of the problems relating to cancer," he told me, "are fundamental ones which concern the cell as such, and we never know what new contribution to basic knowledge may affect profoundly our understanding of cancer." This basic approach was well seen when, some years later, Cowdry published his book, *Cancer Cells*, now a classic in the field.

Cowdry already had published two editions of *A Textbook of Histology* and now was working on a new revision of the book, besides carrying on his numerous other activities. This book differed from many of the older ones on histology in that it made a functional approach to the subject and stressed function of *living* cells, rather than being largely confined to the structure of fixed and dead cells.

It had been a long and profitable day for me. As I took my leave of Doctor Cowdry, I did not realize how many times in the future we would meet again, for such meetings were to occur in many cities of our own country from Miami Beach to San Francisco as well as in Mexico City, London, Merano, Rome and Venice. Nor did I know that some years later I would be serving as a visiting professor of anatomy in his department. Least, of all, however, did I realize, knowing the many achievements and what then seemed to me the long career of Doctor Cowdry, how much of his real work and distinction lay in the years still ahead. For this was before the time of his tremendous work in the organization and administration of the great international congresses in the fields of cancer and of aging, when he was to act as president of the Fourth International Cancer Research Congress in 1947, of the Second International Gerontological Congress in 1951, of the International Association of Gerontology, 1951-54, and as honorary president of the First Pan American Gerontological Congress, 1956 and of the First Pan American Cancer Cytology Congress, 1957.

As I write these lines, I think of my most recent letter from

Doctor Cowdry. It informs me that he is about to leave on a trip to the Far East, and around the world, on a series of scientific visits. His career is still in full swing!

Chapter 11

THE STORK CALLER

A Visit to Doctor Edmond J. Farris

ANATOMY, like the ancient god Janus, has two faces. One of these looks toward the healing arts and serves, as a dignified handmaiden, the fields of surgery and medicine, for which an exact and detailed knowledge of the structure of the human body must be kept ever at hand. The other face of anatomy looks also toward structural detail but, like the penetrating beams of an x-ray tube, pierces through the structure of the human body to the deeper-lying biological truths which concern the vast world of living creatures and which tie them together in a unity resting upon their common lineage in the mysterious process of organic evolution.

In the late nineteenth century the rapid increase in the number of medical schools in the United States, many of them established, shameful to say, largely for pecuniary profit, was tending to submerge the broader aspects of anatomy and to make the field almost entirely subservient to the practical aspects of medical art. Frequently a professorship in anatomy was used to serve only as a stepping-stone to one in surgery. The preservation and the progress of anatomy as a science, under such conditions, owed a great deal to men who were working not only in the field of human anatomy but also in the broader realm of comparative anatomy.

Under the circumstances, the nature of the Wistar Institute of Anatomy and Biology in Philadelphia and particularly the character and philosophy of the men who aided in its establishment are particularly worthy of note, for the Wistar Institute

FIGURE 21 Edmond J. Farris.

was the first anatomical research institution to be established
in this country.

The name "Wistar" was already an old and revered one in the
field of anatomy. Caspar Wistar, a Philadelphian by birth and
a graduate of the University of Pennsylvania, had gone to
Edinburgh for his medical education and had received his Doctor of Medicine degree there in 1786. He had been elected in
two successive years to the presidency of the Royal Medical
Society. The breadth of his interest had taken him deeply into
the study of comparative anatomy, and he had been elected

also to be president of the Edinburgh Society for the Further Investigation of Natural History.

Four years of study abroad had made Doctor Wistar familiar with the work of anatomists and medical men in Edinburgh and London and with the methods of teaching employed by such eminent figures as the members of the Monro "dynasty" of anatomy professors at Edinburgh (father, son and grandson in succession!) and the Hunter brothers in London.

On his return to Philadelphia in 1792, he received the appointment as adjunct professor of anatomy at the University of Pennsylvania and in 1808 became professor of anatomy, a position which he held until his death in 1818. During his long and successful career, he did a great deal to raise the standards of anatomical teaching and science. He wrote the first American system of *Human Anatomy*, a work which continued through several editions. At the time of his death he was serving as president of the American Philosophical Society.

Like many professors, Wistar was a collector or accumulator. The anatomical preparations which he made or obtained gradually grew into a large and valuable collection. His widow presented the collection to the University of Pennsylvania, and under his successors in the chair of anatomy—physick, Professors Horner and Leidy—it continued to grow in size and value. In 1892 it was incorporated as the Wistar Institute of Anatomy and Biology. It was named for Caspar Wistar, but another Wistar played a leading role in its establishment: Isaac, his grandnephew.

General Isaac Wistar, at the time president of the Academy of Natural Sciences of Philadelphia, was a colorful and forceful character. He had been a trailblazer in the virgin wilderness of the Northwest. He had played the roles of miner, trapper, Indian fighter, speculator, lawyer and officer in the Union Army. He furnished funds for a building and endowment for the Institute. Thus it was that on May 21, 1894, a fine new building, housing the Museum and Institute, was formally opened at Woodland Avenue and 36th Street, only a few blocks from the campus of the University of Pennsylvania.

It was at a national meeting of the American Association of Anatomists that I first heard of the Wistar Institute Project on Aging and of the organization of this project by the executive director of the Institute, Doctor Edmond J. Farris. I had been working for several years on age changes in the organs of pedigreed mice, particularly on the cells of the brain. It was not easy, however, to obtain old animals, for a large number of young ones would need to be raised to insure survival of even a few to an advanced age. In addition to this problem, there were a number of other ones, relating to the maintenance of uniform, standard conditions. I understood also that the few other persons who were working in the field at that time were having similar difficulties.

The Wistar Institute was very well known for its excellent colony of pedigreed rats, and the rumor that in some way this colony might be used in the field of studies on aging was indeed an exciting one.

A former director of the Wistar Institute, Doctor H. H. Donaldson, had built up a large colony of albino rats, kept under the finest of laboratory conditions. His great project, a study of the growth of the nervous system and of its parts, had required such a colony to furnish his research materials. As a result of the intensive character of his studies and of those of some of his colleagues, it was actually true that more reliable data had been accumulated bearing upon the life history of this particular mammal than upon that of any other species, man not excepted! Many characteristics of the rat help to make it an almost ideal animal for intensive, well-controlled studies.

As I heard the story, Doctor Farris had received a grant of considerable proportions from Samuel S. Fels, the soap magnate, to carry the study of these animals into the period of old age and thus to obtain as complete a picture as possible of the senescence of one type of laboratory mammal. Also, the plan was to include cooperative work by investigators outside of the Wistar Institute.

I called Farris, and we arranged to meet at one of the social events of the congress. It was in this way my association with one of the ablest anatomists and most engaging personalities whom I have known began. That first meeting was brief and businesslike. Edmond J. Farris, a man of somewhat less than average height, and of fairly robust build, with thick black hair, spectacles and an alert, eager manner, seemed to me to represent a concentration of energy and organizing power seldom seen in a scientific personality. He outlined the plan rapidly and clearly.

Some twenty recognized anatomists, in various parts of the United States, were to be assigned individual organs of the Wistar Institute rats. At stated times, a number of rats of given age would be sacrificed and autopsied at the Institute. The persons carrying out the autopsies would be trained biologists who would make detailed notes and records on the gross appearances seen when the animals were opened. All organs would be accurately weighed. The preparation of the tissues would be as careful as possible, and they would then be shipped, in formalin or in alcohol, to the assigned investigator. There would be also, of course, individual records on these animals made during their lives at the Institute, a fact of particular interest for the aged specimens. If I wanted "in," I would receive the parncreas and the salivary glands. I would have preferred some other organs, such as the nervous tissue, on which I had more background, or the endocrine glands, which were perhaps more exotic, but actually I was something of a Johnny-come-lately on the project, and there was not too much of the rat left! As it turned out over the years, many investigators had to abandon their portions of the project, and I worked not only on the originally assigned organs but also on spleen, lymph nodes, skin and kidney. Even at the present time, my laboratory has thousands of sildes in preparation, serial sections of the spinal cords of some of these animals. At this first conference Doctor Farris told me that he would be very happy to have the cooperating investigators come to visit the Wistar Institute, to see the colony of living animals, and to learn more about other projects going on there.

* * *

It was only a few months later, on a return trip from the

Marine Biological Laboratory at Wood's Hole, Massachusetts, that I did visit Doctor Farris in Philadelphia.

The Wistar Institute of Anatomy and Biology is located in a busy part of Philadelphia but only a few short blocks from the campus of the University of Pennsylvania. As we approached the large building, we found its appearance what we might call interesting but not prepossessing. It sat flush upon the sidewalk, with no green to break the transition from cement to stone. Its three stories showed little attempt at decorative effect, although a rounding of one corner did interrupt the angled monotony.

The main doorway, through which I entered the building, was an arched one, reached by ascending four or five stairs. Just inside, I paused for a moment. Here the architecture was imposing. The hallway, really a spacious lobby, was the full three stories in height, and a broad stairway wound upwards to the second and third floors. To the left was the entrance to the large museum room, to the right a door leading into publication offices and straight ahead the offices of the executive director.

I passed through the central doorway and was met by one of the secretaries. "Doctor Farris is expecting you," she said, and led me on into his office. To say that I was surprised by what I saw would be an understatement. I had been used to quarters for scientific men which generally were small and overcrowded and not infrequently somewhat cluttered and disorderly. Here, however, a great breadth of soft red carpet stretched between me and the broad desk behind which Farris sat. He rose, smiling, and came around the desk to greet me. "I am delighted that you could come," he said. "I hope that you will have time to see a few of the things which we are trying to do here."

I knew, in a general way, that Farris, using the excellent rat colony, had been making some fundamental studies on reproduction and that his interests extended to the problems of sterility in human beings, the sad condition which leaves many couples childless and with a feeling of lack of fulfillment of their marriage. I asked him if I might see something of this work and of his progress in it. "Why, yes," he said. "Let us look into our laboratories where we are studying reproduction, and later on we can talk about the project on aging." Just off from the large office was a series of laboratories where the active work was in progress. "We are attacking the problem from both sides," Farris said, "from the side of the ovum and from that of the sperm. After all, the whole question is one of bringing together these two cells to form a new individual."

From the standpoint of the egg, or ovum, the most important things to determine are where the cell is formed and developed and when it will leave the ovary. For, almost immediately after it leaves this organ, it enters the hollow oviduct and here it is available, ready to be fertilized by the sperm. The act by which the ovum leaves the surface of the ovary is a somewhat dramatic one, for it is contained originally in a follicle, a sort of blister which actually has to burst to liberate this very important cell. "Many investigators have tried in various ways," Farris was saying, "to determine for individual women just when the ovum has been released. But we think that, using our own Wistar rats, we have a really sound method." We entered a small room in which a young lady was leaning over an anesthetized rat. Its abdomen had been opened to expose the ovaries of the immature animal, and she was observing them under a microscope of low magnifying power.

"She is working with our rat hyperemia test," my host explained. "Here the occurrence of human ovulation is detected by what happens to the ovary of an immature rat when urine of the human patient is injected beneath the skin of the rat. If ovulation is not taking place in the human female, the ovary of the rat, examined by opening the animal, shows no effect. If ovulation *is taking place* the hormone content in the human urine brings about an increased prominence of the blood vessels of the ovary of the rat, a hyperemia or excessive amount of blood in the organ, easily visible to the investigator."

"In this way," said my host, "we first determine the day of the month on which ovulation is normally occurring in a case where a problem of sterility exists. Then we advise an attempt

FIGURE 22 The coat of arms of the Wister (Wistar) family.

at conception by husband and wife on that particular day of the succeeding month or months, for these processes usually are very regular for any one individual." Just how successful this method was to become was not known at that time, but several years later Farris reported complete success with forty-six women who sought help in this way. All of them became pregnant, and four did so twice.

The majority of scientific methods have to prove themselves against rival ones. About this time the temperature test for ovulation was receiving considerable attention. The curve of the body temperature during a menstrual cycle was said to drop to a minimum at the time that ovulation occurs. Farris was able to make a direct comparison of the temperature test with the rat ovary hyperemia test according to the actual time of conception in a number of women. He determined that the basal body temperature may serve as a method for detecting time of ovulation in only about 45 per cent of cases and hence is far less reliable than the hyperemia method.

"You mentioned that you are attacking the problem of sterility from the side of the male also," I said. "I would think that this would be a rather difficult problem to approach."

"Well, yes," Farris replied "in one sense it is. There is no one particular event on which to pinpoint the time of occurrence, as for the female. Instead, we have a huge number of actively swimming cells or spermatozoa. But we are learning that different male individuals show important differences in numbers of active spermatozoa."

I knew that much of the earlier work on sterility, carried out by practicing urologists, physicians who specialized on problems of the genitourinary tract, had been made by counts of dead and stained spermatozoa.

"The important thing is the number of *active* sperm," Farris said. "In fact, the *degree* of activity of the individual cells can be studied."

We entered another laboratory. Here a technician with a stopwatch was peering through a microscope. She stopped her work as we came in, and we in turn looked into the microscope. The background was a very finely ruled slide, divided in squares by delicate lines. And in the fluid on the slide a multitude of living cells, organisms very much resembling tadpoles, each with a relatively plump head and body, and a long, active tail, were swimming rapidly about. Looking at a scene like this, it seemed not too surprising that early microscopists, like the great van Leeuwenhoek in the Netherlands, had imagined that he could see in the minute sperm the actual embryo, ready formed to begin the new generation.

"It is possible to fix attention on different individuals and time their motion," Farris explained. "Degree of activity of the sperm seems to be of real importance for fertility. However, our chief study is of the *number* of moving cells in a given area." We now could notice, indeed, that while the general scene was one of great activity, there were many cells which were not in motion. The number of active spermatozoa in one cubic centimeter of a moderately fertile man ranges from 83 million to 185 million, and there generally are several cubic centimeters in an ejaculate.

In his studies at the Institute in those days, Farris was accumulating information on ways in which the semen sample of men might be improved, studying in detail the effect of fatigue, of diet, of the endocrine glands and of other factors on the fertility of the male. In 1950 these studies were to result in an important volume *Human Fertility and Problems of the Male.* So important did these studies become in a practical way, for childless couples, that Edmond Farris soon found himself with a large consulting practice. In this task he was aided, as indeed was often necessary from a legal standpoint, by a physician, Douglas P. Murphy, a delightful character and fine partner to aid the biologist with the more practical side of things.

Farris now showed me some of the other investigations which were occupying his attention. One concerned emotional lymphocytosis. Farris had found that anxiety, fear, anger and disappointment will cause a distinct change in the blood picture of healthy persons. There is an increase in the proportion of the lymphocytes (white cells with rounded nuclei) to the total number of white blood cells of all types in the blood. He now was working specifically on the blood picture of athletes just before and during an athletic effort. His studies were on football, basketball, baseball and other games, as well as wrestling and track and his findings were consistently positive. My only suggestion on these studies on emotional changes was that he might expand them to include the spectators, students and old grads alike, before the games!

To his position as executive director of the Wistar Institute, Farris had brought a wide range of biological and anatomical interest. He was the coauthor of a book *The Rat in Laboratory Investigation* and was later to author another entitled *Care and Breeding of Laboratory Animals*. Earlier in his career he had written an *Art Students' Anatomy*.

His personal interest in preparation of anatomical specimens could be seen as he took me through the Wistar Museum. Among his productions was an x-ray film of the body of an adult human being with the arteries injected with an opaque substance. The injection he had done himself in Buffalo and then had transported the specimen some hundreds of miles to the Eastman Kodak Company in Rochester, New York, for the making of this unique x-ray. Here, the very "tree of life," with its branches and twigs penetrating to every part of the body, could be seen.

He showed me the room in which was kept the famous film collection of the Institute, many items of which are invaluable aids in teaching. Farris himself had done much to further biological photography, especially on living cells, and had served as president of the Biological Photographical Association.

Back in his office, we talked for awhile about personal histories and viewpoints. Farris received his Ph.D. degree at the University of Pennsylvania. He had also gone far toward a medical degree, but his love always had been basic science. He told me that he felt that pure science requires a rather rare combination of qualities—curiosity, originality, perseverance and courage. In his opinion, the medical man usually does not need to have the thoroughness of the pure scientist.

I had been in the institute only a few hours, but I felt that I had come to know a good deal about it and that I had caught some of the enthusiasm which Farris showed when he spoke of its activities. He went with me to the doorway. "In a year or so we may be meeting here in Philadelphia to discuss the progress of our studies on aging," he said, "and I shall look forward to seeing you then."

As I walked away, I felt that the Wistar Institute and all that it stood for in our field of science, was in most capable hands!

Farris' honors, distinctions and citations have been many, yet during that visit and on many an occasion since, I have been struck by his modesty and lack of effort to stress his own accomplishments. Not long ago he told me that the greatest real satisfaction which he has obtained from his research has been the opportunity to aid childless couples to find the joy of parenthood. It was, of course, his basic studies on the seeds of life, the sperm and egg, which have given him this opportunity, and which have led us to entitle this narrative "The Stork Caller"!

Chapter 12

A CLEARING IN THE JUNGLE

A Visit to Doctor Neil P. Macphail at Quiriguá

OUR TRIP to Guatemala had held many surprises. It could hardly have been otherwise, since we had not been able to find out too much about either the route or mode of transportation which we would take until we were well under way. It was in Mexico City, in fact, that we did decide to continue by rail and to see the country between the Mexican and Guatemalan capitals.

Mexico City itself had numerous attractions for us. It had been our first travel goal outside of our own country. In the previous summer we had spent a month there, strolling on its broad avenues and in its beautiful parks and tramping on dusty paths to shrines and historical monuments on its outskirts. The Alameda, Chapultepec, The Shrine of Guadalupe, the Floating Gardens of Xochimilco—these were familiar places to us now.

Then, too, this year, one of my closet friends of graduate school days—now Doctor Norman McQuown—was living in the metropolis. On this second visit he came to greet us at our hotel, a comfortable but definitely second-rate place with artificial leopard-skins thrown over the furniture of its too-ornate lobby. We spent a good deal of time together during the few days of our stay. Norman was a student of languages. He was working now on a most interesting assignment, the creation of written languages from the spoken languages of some of the Indian tribes. In this work his knowledge of phonetics and of comparative grammar was highly useful. As we talked about his present work, I could remember clearly what an assiduous

FIGURE 23 Neil P. Macphail.

scholar he had seemed to be at the University and how he had
stimulated me to learn Esperanto and to correspond with other
enthusiasts of this international language in many parts of
the world.

Doctor McQuown had never been in Guatemala, and I shall
confess that we were a little thrilled to think that even to him,
with his knowledge of Mexican life, our projected journey was
one which would take us into the "great and unknown beyond."
The ticket agents at the railway station, however, were entirely matter of fact. "Yes, you can buy round trip tickets, with
sleeper accommodations, to Guatemala City. Why, you can go
by way of Vera Cruz and through Tehuantepec, to Suchiate,

across the river to the town of Ayutla in Guatemala and then
up to the Highlands and the capital." The first-class fare was
very reasonable, and, modest as our budget was, it suited it
perfectly.

From the City of Mexico to Vera Cruz, the trip was full of the
greatest interest for us. The singular flatness of the terrain just
to the east of the city reminded us of the once great extent of
the Lake of Texcoco, the scene of thriving Aztec communities
when Cortez and his party reached this region. We passed the
district where the Tlascalans, Indians who had joined with the
invaders against the Aztecs, had dwelt. Had all of the Indian
nations stood firmly together, how different might have been
the fate of the Spanish expedition!

We were, indeed, almost retracing the steps of the conquerer,
for we soon began to descend into the rugged jungle country
up which he had made his way from the coast. The train passed
within view of the huge, snow-capped peak of Orizaba, with
its base thickly carpeted by jungle.

We spent a part of our time outside on the rear platform,
where, as from the stern of a ship, we could view the "wake" of
our vehicle. The analogy may be considered a more apt one
when we add that, like a ship, we were followed by birds,
wheeling and turning in the clear blue sky. These were not the
white gulls of the sea, however, but huge vultures, scavengers,
watching for the rubbish thrown over the side by the kitchen
help or others on the train.

Vera Cruz was reached before evening, and there we spent
two nights and a day. Our hotel room was situated directly
opposite the belltower of the cathedral, a fact which was made
painfully apparent at 5:30 A.M. the first morning when its
sound fairly filled our room. At least, I have never known a
more efficient alarm clock!

From Vera Cruz to the Guatemalan border, the journey was one
which we had anticipated with at least some misgiving, chiefly
because we had found no one in our circle of acquaintances who
had made it or who had any firsthand information on it. True,
we were to pass through one of the most interesting parts of

Mexico, the Isthmus of Tehuantepec. Here were the sites of great civilized communities, the armies of which had fought bloody wars with the Aztecs. Here in modern times were picturesque villages, colorful natives and a peaceful, tradition-bound way of life. But here also were heat and mosquitoes and jungles.

Any trepidation which we might have had about the trip was soon dispelled. The train coach was entirely screened from insect pests, the seats were comfortable and the attitude of the conductors, stewards and porters was friendly and helpful. The jungle really only added to the pleasure of the trip. True, it was close enough, for much of the time the train moved along between high walls of dense green vegetation, splashed here and there with the brilliant hues of orchids and other blossoms. But its bad features—and we learned later that they are fewer than is generally advertised—were effectively shut off from us, while we had opportunity to catch close-up views of strange birds and mammals, or brilliant insects.

The train stops were truly occasions. As we drew into a village, we would find the tracks lined with what seemed to be practically its entire population. Brilliantly clad Indian men and women and naked children, *mestizos* (Spanish Mexicans) and innumerable dogs were out to greet us. It is not, however, curiosity nor hospitality which prompts this gathering along the railroad, but rather the very spirit of commerce—the needs of the train passengers and the ability of the villagers to supply those needs. Actually, the great consumers in this spectacle of trade are the passengers on second and third class coaches where the contact with the outside is easier (no screens!) and where the amenities of the train's kitchen are, because of prices, beyond the reach of many of the travellers. This is not to say, however, that the train's kitchen itself does not receive some fine additions to the larder at these stops, for we saw many live chickens, fresh fruits and vegetables being purchased on the spot by those in charge of food preparation.

Fruits, flowers, cold drinks, merchandise of most varied kinds, were lifted up to the eager hands of passengers along the train, and silver and copper coins passed to the villagers. It seemed a pleasant, almost a gala, occasion. And then we would be off again, the jungle closing in along the tracks.

We were not without good companions. A handsome young couple returning to Honduras after a vacation in Mexico City were most friendly and communicative, and a middle-aged Mexican gentleman with a good sense of humor made us a party of five. Such companionship was a very salutary thing for our somewhat adolescent Spanish. There was in our coach also an American tourist, a woman somewhat on the portly side, with a knowledge of Spanish far more rudimentary than our own. She had plans to leave the train at Tapachula, a town a considerable distance from the border, to stay there overnight, and to travel on by bus across the border the next day. Our Mexican friend seemed to get a "charge" out of telling her how dirty and unsociable a place Tapachula was, and our Honduran friends joined in with him in urging her to stay on the train until we reached the border at Suchiate. *"Tapachula muy sucio, muy feo, Suchiate limpio,"* the Mexican would tell her and accompany the description with very appropriate facial expressions. But she was a strong-willed lady and, sure enough, at Tapachula just about dusk, she left us.

We spent the night in Suchiate. Our three companions and we had dinner together at the guesthouse, a copious meal washed down with peach brandy, a bottle of which the Mexican had produced. In spite of a terrific tropical storm, we slept well and awoke refreshed for the crossing of the frontier. This crossing was far more interesting than we might have expected. We and our bags were piled into primitive boats and poled across the broad river. A few hundred feet from the opposite shore we were led into the customs house, a large palm-thatched hut, open on one side.

Soon we were on the Guatemalan train and off again through country very similar to that which we had traversed in southern Mexico. Again the stops at the villages were the occasion for much commerce. At one of these we bought green coconuts, and the vendor proceeded to slice them open with great sweeps of his machete so that we could drink the cool, rich milk within.

The aspect of the country changed as we ascended into the hills, and soon the air began to feel dry and bracing. Guatemala City itself lies at an altitude of 4,877 feet, and its climate is similar to that of Mexico City. As we rode from the station to a hotel, we saw wide streets lined by modern buildings and throngs of people seemingly as intent on their business as in the larger cities of our own country.

The capital city of Guatemala served as our home and headquarters for almost a month. We learned much about Guatemala within the city, visiting its parks, museums, and public buildings, and from it we made journeys to Chimaltenango, Quetzaltenango, Antigua and other cities. In Antigua, once capital of Guatemala, and a center of Spanish culture in the western hemisphere, we wandered among the ruins of massive colonial buildings destroyed by the disastrous earthquakes which caused the government to move from here in 1776. On the stairs of the cathedral in this city we came upon an old friend, the American tourist lady! She obviously had survived Tapachula and seemed in fine fettle.

Our home in Guatemala City, after the first night, was a delightful place, the Pension Gueroult, a lodging house with the most exquisite and verdant patio which we had ever seen. Here birds sang in the leafy coverts, a fountain tinkled, and a cool retreat was always available. The food was excellent and the proprietor a man of culture—a host in the truest sense of the word.

❋   ❋   ❋

We had written to the Hospital of the United Fruit Company at Quiriguá soon after our arrival in the capital. Our reading as we prepared for the trip had made us well acquainted with the name of Doctor Neil P. Macphail, Director of the Hospital, and we were most pleased to receive from him an invitation to visit Quiriguá.

We went by train from Guatemala City, an interesting trip, a large portion of which carried us through lush tropical country along the Rio Motagua. On this journey we met and talked with a young Frenchman—an individual who somehow carried with him a subtle air of quiet excitement. We could not help feeling ourselves in a sort of cloak-and-dagger atmosphere in his presence. It was early in his career but he was on his way, for this man turned out to be none other than Jacques Soustelle, an authority on pre-Columbian history, later to become the righ-hand man of General Charles DeGaulle.

Tea was at Zacapa, a stop enlivened only by our French friend's conversation.

At the little station of Quiriguá, we were met by a tall, bronzed man in boots and field clothes, wearing a broad-brimmed hat. This was Mr. Fred Clark, a foreman for the United Fruit Company. "Welcome to Quiriguá!" he said, "I am to take you to Doctor Macphail." We got into a truck and drove a short distance down the road. Suddenly ahead of us the jungle cleared and we saw a great stretch of well-kept lawn sloping upwards to the Hospital. The rays of the late afternoon sun picked out the windows in the white front of the long, two-story building. Stately palm trees stood at wide intervals along the front of the Hospital. We drove up to the main entrance. At the door of the director's office we were greeted by Doctor Macphail. Distinguished, courtly, but warm and friendly, he put us at ease immediately. His silvering hair was parted neatly on one side. His features were rugged yet refined—a long oval face, with twinkling eyes surmounted by full, dark eyebrows, a nose of ample size, a strong mouth and a firm jaw.

Macphail was a real product of Scotland. Born on March 22, 1882, on the Isle of Mull in Argyllshire—one of the famous Western Isles of Doctor Samuel Johnson's pilgrimage with James Boswell—he was educated at the University of Aberdeen, where he received his medical diploma in 1906. But this man in immaculate white had adapted himself to the Tropics—had seen their beauties and their snares, which entrap many from the temperate zones. He had learned to love their beauties and to avoid or conquer their snares.

We talked for awhile in his office. Then he took us on a quiet tour of the Hospital—a very informal rounds, in which the role of the patients, or of those who were awake, was only to respond to his cheerful greeting. The Hospital, opened in 1913, had a capacity of 250 beds. It had been made as secure as possible against fire and earthquakes. As our host showed us some of the details of these safeguards in the walls and foundations, he said, "Earthquakes in this country are a very real danger. The catastrophe up in the capital back in 1918 made thousands homeless, and the roads out were jammed with the fleeing people." I thought of some of the original photographs of this quake which we had seen in a shop in Guatemala City and also of the terrific destruction which had visited Antigua, the old capital.

FIGURE 24 A stela of the ancient Mayas. Quiriguá, Guatemala.

We speak often of the personal relationship between physician and patient. Here was a most conspicuous evidence of how strong and meaningful this relationship can be, for to the patient at the Quiriguá Hospital, Doctor Macphail seemed to be a father and physician combined.

The records of the Hospital showed some of the remarkable progress made here against disease. When the Hospital was established, malaria drew a dark shadow over all of this part of Guatemala. A common form here was the dread Motagua fever, which for many years had a mortality of almost 100 per cent in the holdings of the United Fruit Company along the Motagua River. In those days, the incidence of malaria was actually between seventy and eighty per cent of the population. The records showed that by now it had decreased to a little over five per cent!

Macphail said to us, "The fight against malaria is not one which can be won in the hospital or clinic alone. We have had to get out into the field, to inspect the living conditions of the workers and their families. Every possible breeding place for mosquitoes is a menace, and this fact must be repeated over and over again to impress it on the people's minds. Then adequate screening of houses and beds must be furnished and its use promoted."

While there were many types of cases in the Hospital, Macphail's chief efforts, besides the anti-malarial work, have been against intestinal parasitism and against malnutrition. The efforts of the director and staff among the people had led to better homes, more adequate sanitary facilities, safer means of food preparation and more varied diet, and thus to a great decrease in mortality. "Yes, we have had very many children come into the world in this Hospital," said Doctor Macphail in reply to our question. "And the records of our maternity cases compare well with those of hospitals in the temperate zones."

He now led us to a simple but comfortable room, one which resembled the private rooms of the Hospital—indeed, it was one of these, vacant at the time. Here we were to stay overnight. The doctor looked at his watch. "I have a few things to do to wind up the day," he said. "May I see you for dinner in about an hour?"

After a rest, we walked along the wide, glassed-in veranda to the front of the doctor's quarters. Here we sat with Macphail and two of the members of his medical staff as the tropical dusk deepened. It was very much like a scene from a story of the Tropics, even to the tall drinks served us, to the silhouettes of the palms and to the distant hills beyond the Motagua. "Over there," said Doctor Macphail, gesturing toward the south and the rolling hills, "lies Honduras, and not far away are the ruins of Copán." The time passed very pleasantly, and after awhile we went in to dinner. The food was excellent and the atmosphere one of refined taste and leisure. When, after liqueurs on the veranda, we retired to our own room, we had no trouble in sinking into sleep.

*　*　*

We slept very well after our long day and were up early, for we had a rendezvous with Fred Clark—and with the ancient past. Today we were to visit the ruins at Quiriguá. In some ways, it seems wrong to call these Mayan structures ruins, for the *stelae* and other massive sculptured stones have retained so well the human faces and animal forms that the passage of time cannot be said to have ruined them. We rode the mile or so to the archaeological site on a narrow gauge railway. Quiriguá was one of the great Mayan centers in the time of the Old Empire and appears to have been flourishing about 500 A.D. when Europe was in the grip of the Dark Ages. The ancient cities can be dated with considerable accuracy because of the erection of the *stelae*, elaborately carved stone columns which bear the dates of their erection in the complex hieroglyphics of the Mayans. Over one thousand of these *stelae* have been discovered, chiefly in the jungles of Guatemala and southern Mexico! They are carved on one, two, three or even four sides, and the front usually shows a representation of what may be a god or a man of high station, a priest or monarch.

We left the little train and passed through a narrow belt of jungle. Suddenly we were in a clearing and among the wonders of the past. A *stela* over twenty feet high rose before us, its carved figures etched in sharp relief in the tropical sunlight. The figure of a man occupied most of the side facing us. The trunk and limbs were in low relief, but the face and headdress were deeply carved. The effect was striking and the person, or possibly deity, seemed to be looking directly at us from across the centuries. His costume was elaborate, and he bore a peculiar hooked object, perhaps a symbol of authority. Particularly strange was the high headdress, somewhat reminiscent of that of the Egyptian pharaohs. As we approached the huge column, we saw that its sides were covered by square hieroglyphic characters, two long rows on each side of the *stela*. On the rear was more carving, not even a small portion of the hard stone being left unworked.

Other *stelae* stood in clearings nearby. One was crowned by a great mass of feathers, the delicate objects so realistically carved from the stone as to suggest the very texture of a plumed head-dress. Another presented a rectangular niche with a finely formed human figure squatting in Buddhist fashion, with magnificent featherwork all about him (Fig. 24).

Besides the *stelae* there were many bulky masses which appear to have been enormous boulders chiselled into the form of monstrous animals, real or imaginary. On the sides of these creatures, again there appeared the hieroglyphics, and part of these, again, gave the dates of the work. One such figure was weird indeed, for from the animal body a human head protruded, as though from its very jaws.

We learned that the dates carved at Quiriguá represent a span of hundreds of years, for *Stela A* bore the date of 176 A.D. Many generations had come and gone here and left their amazing work, and a host of baffling and intriguing questions for the historian, the archaelogist, and the ethnologist to study. For, despite the solidity of these remains of a great civilization, the nature and origin of the people who built them are lost in the mists of antiquity. It seems probable that when this civilization was at its peak the climatic conditions here may have been more favorable. But theories as to the reason for the decline of the Mayans include also exhaustion of the soil from repeated plant-ings, invasion by alien peoples and a number of other ideas, none of which, however, can be said to be much more than hypothesis. Especially intriguing are some of the speculations of a possible relationship between the civilizations of ancient America and those of the Old World or even of the lost Atlantis! That such a degree of culture could have arisen in the New World in complete isolation, or that many of its inventions and customs might resemble those of the Old World only through parallel, but separate, development may seem even harder to believe than that somewhere in the remote past a communication existed.

We returned to the Hospital for the noon meal, for we were to take the afternoon train to Guatemala City. Doctor Macphail came down to bid us a good trip and to invite us to come again to the clearing in the jungle.

✿   ✿   ✿

It is many years since our visit to Quiriguá. Some time ago we heard of the passing of Doctor Macphail and a little later of the erection of a bust, carved in Guatemala marble by the sculptor Rodolfo Galeotti Torres, on the scenic grounds of the hospital.

I have seen a picture of the bust and the fine monument on which it is raised some twenty feet above the ground. In a way, it is another *stela;* but in this case we know clearly the reason for its erection. It is a symbol of the gratitude and love of a people for a great and unselfish laborer in the vineyard.

Chapter 13

SCIENTIST OF JAPAN
A Visit to Doctor Tsunetaro Fujita

"**G**O-JU GO fun." This was indeed a rather strange phrase to be coming to my ears, but perhaps more strange was the fact that I understood this much of the sentence as meaning fifty-five minutes. It was part of an announcement from the cabin of our Japan Airlines plane telling us, in Japanese, and then in English, that we would arrive in Honolulu in eight hours and fifty-five minutes. Having anticipated for several months this journey across the Pacific, I had spent a little time with phrase books, records and other aids to the intricacies of the Japanese language.

During the two years past, the opportunity to meet some of the outstanding professors of anatomy from Japan had come my way, through their attendance at an international meeting in New York and visits also to our own department at Indiana University. Now, with my wife and daughter, I was making a travel dream, a journey to the Far East, come true, and was looking forward to seeing some of these scientific friends in their own laboratories.

Even in the plane we had found ourselves in a new and exotic environment. The stewardesses were kimono-clad figures of dainty and exquisite beauty. It seemed that the majority of the passengers were Japanese, with a number of other Asiatic countries represented and but few Americans or Europeans. Rice, eggrolls and Japanese tea and cookies were a prominent part of the ample snacks provided aboard.

Honolulu International Airport was a busy scene when we arrived at a few minutes before 1 A.M. "Aloha" in huge electric

150

FIGURE 25 Tsunetaro Fujita.

letters greeted us, and in the sky-room we had complimentary fresh pineapple. There was one cause for real concern—no leis! Our daughter, Nancy, had come to think of a welcome to Hawaii as incomplete without a lei being dropped about one's neck, or at least without a lei which one could drop about one's own neck! So we scouted about. I picked up the first one—a rather sadly wilted thing which someone had left at the International

Shoe Shine Stand. Then we found a fresher one, and another, and within a short time, all three of us were well-provided. A little over an hour later we were taking off again, ready for our plane to put more and more miles behind us. It was at 3:40 A.M. that we crossed the International Date Line, thus jumbling yesterday, today and tomorrow together on this August 11, 1960, in the Year of Nezumi, the Rat.

*   *   *

It was morning. We were flying above a light cloud field. Then we began to descend and between the fleecy white patches we caught glimpses of a strange new land—Honshu, Japan! We could see the shores and the waters of a great harbor, thronged with ships. This, then, was Tokyo Bay where, almost fifteen years before, an armada of American and British warships had assembled and where, on the greatest of them, the Missouri, the document of surrender had been signed. Here, on September 2, 1945, General MacArthur had spoken briefly, with dignity but without rancor, of the path ahead for this still great nation, a path along which he was to prove a stern yet helpful guide.

We knew that not all was tranquil and calm in the "island country," even as we had planned our journey and as we now approached. Only short weeks before, at Haneda, the airport where we soon would be landing, the person of the President's press secretary, Mr. James Haggerty, had been placed in very real danger when his car was surrounded by overzealous Japanese partisans protesting the signing of a mutual security treaty —and the President's own visit had been cancelled. As our plane put down on the runway at Haneda, we could not help feeling a bit of relief that we had no diplomatic mission to perform. As it was, the only thing inimical to us that morning was the heat. Our bags moved swiftly through customs, and in minutes we were being driven past the great Japan Airlines Building and along the road toward the city. Many laborers, men and women, with neckerchiefs about their heads, were at work along the highway. Signs became more numerous, the large Kanji, or Chinese characters, alternating with the somewhat lighter ones of the two Japanses syllabaries, the Katakana and Hiragana, all of them intriguing and mysterious to us.

Now we were in among the streets. Most of the houses were two stories, and chiefly of wood. Here and there were groups of Gingko trees and of sycamores. At places along the route we saw interesting stone images of lions and other animals before the houses. Traffic was abundant enough, but by no means chaotic. As we neared the center, modern skyscrapers came into view. Soon we stopped at the entrance to our hotel—the Dai Ichi, literally, "The great or outstanding one."

The lobby was a busy scene and a wonderful mixture of oriental and occidental costumes. But we had scarcely entered when a distinguished-appearing Japanese rose from a chair and came toward us.

Professor Tsunetaro Fujita was a man in his middle fifties, serious and dignified in mien, with a look of disciplined intellectual acuity. Greying hair was brushed back from a high forehead. Heavy dark eyebrows accentuated the smoothness of his features. He wore narrow-rimmed spectacles, a white shirt with long tie, and a well-fitting suit of European type.

It was only a few months earlier that I had last seen and talked with Professor Fujita. He had been serving as chief delegate of the Japanese Association of Anatomists at the Seventh International Anatomical Congress in New York City. It was there that I told him of our plan to visit Japan and that he had invited me to pay an official visit to the Medical School of the University of Tokyo and to give a talk there during our stay.

It was indeed a pleasure, this many thousands of miles from New York, to see our host and to have the warm associations come to mind of the other occasions, in the States, when we had met. Actually, Professor Fujita had been a long-term associate of another friend of mine, Doctor Hartwig Kuhlenbeck, Professor of Anatomy at the Woman's Medical College of Pennsylvania and author of the great work, *Mind and Matter.*

Professer Kuhlenbeck had been Fujita's teacher at the Tokyo Imperial University (the present University of Tokyo) some time before 1930 and again had been his professor some years later in Breslau, Germany, while Fujita was spending two years in that country. In those days, the German universities were Meccas for many intellectually eager Japanese scholars.

We sat in a comfortable corner of the lobby, talked for a short while and made arrangements for my visit to the University of Tokyo Medical School. This was Friday, a little after noon. I was to be at the medical school on Monday, to present a talk there on Monday afternoon, and to attend a reception by the faculty later that day.

Professor Fujita insisted that he would call for me on Monday, and we parted with a "sayonara."

※　※　※

The rest of that day and most of the two succeeding days were devoted chiefly to what might be called sightseeing. It was, however, highly individualized and carried out with the help and the company of Japanese friends. One of these, Doctor Gan Sakakibara, is a professor of economics at Aoyama University. He had met us at Haneda and promised to come back to the hotel for us after we had a little rest.

With Professor and Mrs. Sakakibara, we left the hotel and started out for a really popular style restaurant. This was our first experience with a regular Japanese cabdriver, and as one breathless escape followed another, we could almost agree with our twelve-year-old daughter's remark that he probably was "a former suicide pilot"!

The restaurant was small, but it was divided into two parts. The first part, where we were seated, had an L-shaped counter, along which chairs were ranged, while the second, behind us, contained a platform raised several feet above the floor, with two tables on it for dining. Our hosts had seated us at the counter in order that we could see what went on behind it. And indeed it was well worth while to have this point of vantage! Behind the counter was a Japanese lady of middle age and of really somewhat formidable mien. In fact, she reminded us strongly of the colorful Bloody Mary in *South Pacific!* A patch over one eye only added to the impression which she made upon the three of us. This "mistress of ceremonies" was presiding

over the sacred rite of preparation of the tempura, a favorite
Japanese dish. A huge bowl of oil was set out, and then "Mary"
began to prepare a strange assortment of items, including many
small fish, large shrimp and miscellaneous fragments of molluscs.
These she rolled in batter and dropped in the oil for a rather
casual cooking. Soon, bowls of rice, fish, and the other items were
before us, plus—chopsticks! Actually, these latter were a saving
feature, for they helped to take our minds off of the strangeness
of our meal. Our daughter was particularly adept at making a
few rice-grains and some polite conversation obscure the fact
that she was not greedily devouring the flesh of the sea creatures! Actually, aside from its strangeness, the food tasted very
good to me; but I, too, was cautious in regard to the quantity
that I took. The hot green tea seemed to help in neutralizing the
oiliness of the dish.

Luncheon over, we gave our thanks to "Mary" behind the
counter and stepped out onto the streets of Tokyo! We were close
to the great thoroughfare, the Ginza, and so the five of us walked
over and mingled with the throngs moving up and down it. Here
again was a wonderful mixture and blending of the Orient and
Occident, of the old and the new. Brilliant kimonos brushed
against western suits and dresses, and people of many races
seemed at home here.

We visited one of the smart department stores—the Wako,
it was called. One could not distinguish it from a similar em-
porium in New York or Chicago except for the sales persons and
a few of the products.

We were just about to enter the famous Mikimoto's, the home
of the cultured pearls, when the Sakakibaras recognized friends,
a handsome young man and his mother. This was Toro Karutsu,
a former student of Professor Sakakibara at Aoyama University,
out shopping with his mother. It really was somewhat of a
coincidence, as it was Toro who was to take us about Tokyo
the next day.

In Mikimoto's, we saw some of the many methods of using
pearls, talked with the manager about the culture methods and
received a free map of Tokyo.

After a soft drink at a little place called the Olympic, we cabbed back to the Dai Ichi.

The next morning Toro was on hand early. We walked over to the nearby Imperial Hotel to carry out the ever-necessary business of reconfirmation of flight. It was at least a bit of a thrill to hear a Pan American clerk asking another passenger, *"Hong Kong made, ne?"* ("To Hong Kong, is it not so?") and to understand that much. Nancy, Linda and Toro went off to some of the small but very attractive shops in the hotel, and when my business was over I had to set out to find them. Before I did so, however, I found myself coming to the aid of a young American lady by modelling for her a beautiful kimono which she wanted to buy as a present for her father back home.

When we were all together again, I remarked to Toro on the beautiful and exotic architecture of the interior of the Imperial Hotel. In fact, it made me think that it might have been modelled after some ancient city discovered in the deserts of Asia where it had lain buried for thousands of years. "Yes, it is beautiful," said Toro. "It was all planned by a very good American architect!" Frank Lloyd Wright was responsible for it, and he made it earthquake-proof; it was one of the few buildings left after the 1923 disaster.

From the Imperial Hotel the four of us took a cab over to the Imperial Palace, or rather, to its grounds, which are very extensive; the Palace itself is open only upon certain occasions. A tremendous moat, formed of huge stones fitted together roughly, lay before us. Its calm waters were far below, and on its banks stood feathery green pines, much like those we had left so far behind in San Francisco. As we strolled along, we were not by any means alone. Many persons were enjoying the air, and cameras were numerous among the Japanese tourists. In the waters of the canals and moats, great black swans sailed along majestically, and soon, as counterpoint, white birds of the same kind appeared. It was hard to realize that we were in the midst of the largest city on earth, except when we looked from some eminence to see the skyscrapers of the busy streets nearby, or when we caught the sound of rivet hammers from one of the many great projects of construction which were going on.

FIGURE 26 Ivory figure of the Jurojin, the Japanese representation for a long and happy life.

We returned to the Dai Ichi for lunch. Here we had a chance to learn more of our companion, who was a most agreeable young man. He was (and is, I hope) a tenor singer of some ability and the following year was to be studying music in Tacoma, Washington! After lunch and a brief rest, we set out again. We went first to visit a famous center of the Buddhist faith, the Asakusa Shrine. Many things which we saw in Japan surprised us and one of these was this, our first Buddhist shrine. The entrance was through a gateway, guarded by huge and hideous figures, representing the god of thunder and the god of wind—*kami* "divinities," from the Shinto pantheon, rather than the Buddhist. We were reminded of the remarkable conciliation between Shintoism and Buddhism which had taken place in the *Nara* period, and by which these kami had become the avatars of the Buddha! The entrance took us into a covered avenue on either side of which was the most varied and attractive collection of shops that one could imagine. Here were objects of every description, each shop specializing in its own assortment. There were foods of all kinds, jewelry, books, leather products, silk products, statuettes and thousands of charming toys, including many mechanical ones. Among the last was a pair of giant Sumo wrestlers who, at the turn of a switch, would go through some of their most common maneuvers.

Beyond the shops we entered a broad open space. In the center of this was the shrine itself, a great building, badly damaged in the war and now partially restored. We ascended the stairs. A delicate fragrance filled the air all about. Soon we saw its source—a huge iron kettle in which joss sticks were burning. Beyond this was a cubicle where prayer papers could be obtained and contributions received. Priests sat quietly behind a counter.

We made our way around to the rear of the building. There, in an ancient garden, was the largest Gingko tree we had ever seen, and near it was a fine stone statue of the Buddha.

How strange it seemed, after leaving the shrine, to find ourselves descending for a first ride on the Tokyo subway! And how similar in many ways this seemed to that of New York City—

with people absorbed in their newspapers or staring into space!

Our next stop was the famous Mitsukoshi department store, a place of real beauty, graciousness and efficiency. One item, too, this store possessed which is not boasted by any western store—a tremendous figure—the *Tennyo,* "Heavenly Maiden." This creation is five stories high and was ten years in construction. It is an elaborate and intricate structure of shining glass and gleaming lacquer. One could spend many hours in studying its details, but the over-all effect is one—as probably was intended—of dazzling magnificence.

* * *

Nikko is a town some ninety miles north of Tokyo. There is a saying: "Don't say *kekko* ('beautiful') until you have seen Nikko." Nikko is more than the town by that name. Nikko National Park comprises 500 acres, a beautifully scenic expanse of mountains, lakes and waterfalls, with the shrine most sacred to the national history of Japan.

We had left Tokyo in the morning and had sped north by train, accompanied this time by a professional, but most friendly yet unobtrusive guide, a Mr. Kato from Kamakura. After lunch at the small inn or hotel, we took a car for the trip to the great Kegon Falls. A steady upward climb brought us into the region of cool mountain air and mist. The falls leap from a height of ninety-seven meters. Our observation platform was about two hundred meters from the place where they strike, and below us the swift, boiling waters raced by. Scores of tourists, almost all of them Japanese, were enjoying the magnificent view, and, with cameras of many descriptions, were reproducing it on film.

From this view of one of nature's greatest beauties in these beautiful islands, we descended to visit manmade beauties that are yet more impressive. The setting of this sacred region is in the midst of extensive groves of the Japanese cypress or Cryptomeria, huge thick-trunked trees which rise to a height of 125 feet and which impart an air of quiet solemnity to the entire region.

We went by a smooth wide avenue to the temple yards. An

immense *torii,* "gateway," embellished with red lacquer, stands at the entrance, but like all such torii, it is always open.

The temples are Buddhist shrines, massive yet graceful buildings of wood, heavily lacquered and ornamented with exquisitely carved and brilliantly painted figures of many kinds. As we walked among them, we saw many world-renowned carvings. Among them were the three monkeys, or more accurately, apes: *Iwazaru,* he who speaks no evil; *Kikazaru,* he who hears no evil, and *Mizaru,* he who sees no evil. How often had we looked on reproductions of these apes in many parts of the world!

Even more striking and natural is the carving of "The Sleeping Cat," a creation by Jingoro, the greatest of Japanese sculptors. We now were entering a holy building, that which contains the shrine of the shogun, Tokugawa Ieyasu (1542-1616). Ieyasu was the founder of the power of the Tokugawa family, a power which endured in Japan for two and a half centuries.

We passed through a wide hallway on one side of which, behind a table, were seated priests of the Shinto faith, dignified and indeed handsome in their tall ceremonial headwear. Beyond this we entered the quiet of the sanctuary. In this room, abundantly adorned with gold leaf, were three simple chests, closed and locked. These, we were told, contained the clothes of Ieyasu. A few worshippers knelt in silent contemplation at a little shrine.

After a few minutes, we left and made our way back to the great torii and out into the world of modern Japan.

❋ ❋ ❋

Back in Tokyo, we had slept well. Professor Fujita called for me at an early hour, and we took a taxi from the Dai Ichi out to Tokyo University. As we rode along the busy streets, Fujita told me that there were a score or more of medical schools in Tokyo and a number of dental schools. We passed the Tojo Medical and Dental School (The name implies that Hideki Tojo was hardly a war criminal in the eyes of the Japanese.) Not long before we reached the University, we passed the Juntendo Medical School.

As we entered the University grounds, I saw an extensive campus which might well have passed for that of some American university. We stopped before a large building and, leaving the taxi, ascended the stairs and entered. Professor Fujita led me first to the office of the dean, a type of sanctuary very different from that of the shogun at Nikko, yet to be reverenced almost equally by some faculty circles, both in Japan and our own country. The dean who greeted me here was indeed a distinguished person, Doctor Yoshida, a noted pathologist, after whom the Yoshida sarcoma, well known to experimental pathologists the world over, had been named. Dean Yoshida was a strikingly handsome man. In the conference room adjoining his office, we talked of some mutual acquaintances, including the American pathologist, Robert Moore, and the great scientist and organizer, Edmund V. Cowdry. The latter, Dean Yoshida told me, had visited Japan six times. Before we left the conference room, I was shown a model of the proposed library of the school of medicine, to be built with the funds from a grant made by the Rockefeller Foundation.

Doctor Fujita took me now to the laboratory of Professor Nakai, in the department of anatomy. I was surprised as we entered to see a number of pieces of very modern laboratory equipment, including a time-lapse cinematographic camera. I soon learned, however, that not only was Nakai an ardent tissue culturist, but that he had worked for some time with Charles Pomerat at the very well-equipped laboratories of the University of Texas Medical School at Galveston. His work, both in Texas and Tokyo, was with the cells of the nervous system, cultivated outside of the body. He showed me a very comprehensive workbook with hundreds of photomicrographs of the supporting cells of the nervous system, the neuroglia. It was, in fact, a book in preparation and to be called *Atlas of the Neuroglia*. Professor Nakai's laboratory activities had expanded until they invaded and seemed to be taking over the small office in which were his desk and books.

A short way down the hall we entered the office and laboratory of my host, Tsunetaro Fujita. He offered me a chair and excused himself briefly to check with an assistant. As I sat there, my eyes wandered over the books on the shelves nearby. Besides the many anatomical works, there were others of interest. Here was the great set of *Brehm's Tierleben,* a treasury of zoological knowledge, which I myself had almost purchased at one time in Zürich. And, there, to my pleasant surprise, were *Andrew's Comparative Histology* and *Cellular Changes with Age.* It was good to know that the former book had gotten as far as Tokyo. The latter, a rather thin monograph, Doctor Fujita had in the original English, although it had been translated not long before into the Japanese language. (I had received fourteen dollars for the translation rights.)

Near these volumes was an *Atlas of Anatomy* by Professor Fujita. When he returned, I asked him about this. As a matter of fact, I really did not know of a definitive work in anatomy in the Japanese language. "It was my own professor who began the set," he explained, "by writing a volume on *The Skeleton.*" The second volume, covering the anatomy of the head, was done by Fujita, and took him several years to write. On the third volume, *The Abdomen,* he had spent twelve years! The plates were in magnificent color and executed with great artistic skill and anatomical knowledge by illustrators who worked in closest collaboration with the author. Not only had Fujita carried out this immense amount of work on the *Atlas* series, he had completed also a textbook of *Dental Histology* and one of *Dental Anatomy.* Actually, he had taught for seventeen years in dental school.

He next showed me an immense collection of teeth which he had assembled and on which he had reported in research publications. There were hundreds of glass vials, each containing the set of teeth from a single individual. These were from cadavers dissected in the laboratory and reminded me actually of how much potentially important material in such a laboratory is not used as it might be.

Born in Mie perfecture on June 21, 1903, Tsunetaro Fujita was a true son of the rural areas of Japan. Interested in the route which a young Japanese with scientific leanings might follow,

I asked him concerning his early sources of stimulation. He told me, very frankly, "I do not think I have ever been influenced in my childhood and early youth nor inspired to my scientific studies. Born out in the country, I spent all my early days playing with children of farmers without reading, almost without thinking."

In the high school, however, Tsunetaro encountered a teacher of natural history. This man, he felt, was a humble, but genuine scientist. Of him and his attitude toward the students, Tsunetaro said, "He let us know the pleasure of experimental observation." After graduation from the high school he studied medicine at the University of Tokyo Medical School (at that time known as Tokyo Imperial University) and graduated in 1928. It was from 1931 to 1945 that he served as professor of anatomy at the Tokyo Kotoshika Igakko (Tokyo Government Dental School). From 1945 up until my visit (1960) he had been professor of anatomy at the University of Tokyo. He had added a Ph.D. degree to his M.D. in 1934. His thesis, *Periphere Ausbreitung des N. facialis beim Menschen* (*Peripheral distribution of the facial nerve of man*) was published in a German journal, the "Morphologisches Jahrbuch."

"I was very fortunate," Doctor Fujita reminisced. "From early in 1933 until 1935, I was a travelling research fellow of the Japanese Government, studying in Breslau and in Berlin. In Breslau I had the great pleasure of studying again with Professor Kuhlenbeck, under whom I had worked at the Imperial University some years earlier. I visited many of the European countries and then I returned to Japan by way of the United States and Canada. In 1952, I journeyed to the States at the invitation of Doctor Kuhlenbeck and spent six months at the Woman's Medical College in Philadelphia, where he is professor. Again, as you know, I had the honor to revisit America as chief delegate of the Japanese Association of Anatomists to the International Anatomical Congress just last spring."

Fujita's real love of his subject is a trait which soon impresses itself upon one. He has compared the curiosity and the intellectual urge of a scientist to the feelings that spur a mountain

climber on toward the conquest of virgin peaks. The thrill of
the advance upward into the unknown and then the thrill of
accomplishment, of standing upon the lofty eminence and viewing the miles upon miles of new territory are shared alike by
the mountain climber and the true scientist.

* * *

"Let us visit now the library," Fujita said. We went upstairs
and entered the reading room and then the stacks. An oddly
sweet and pleasant fragrance hovered over the rows of books.
The polyglot nature of the collection was more marked than in
most libraries which I had visited in Europe and America, but
many of the old classics of our fields seemed to be present, and
I suppose that the other basic sciences of medicine were as
fortunate.

"If you would like to visit our museum," said Professor Fujita,
"I believe there is still time."

"I certainly would," I replied. "In fact, that is one of the
things to which I have looked forward a great deal."

My anticipation of the museum was amply justified. It was
on an upper floor and comprised a surprisingly large area. A
part of the space was open, with tables and displays, while
another part was occupied with row after row of shelves containing neatly labelled specimens. In several places I saw spec-
tacular objects, which looked not unlike the skins of giant bats.
Oddly, however, they were of many colors and covered with
curious designs. A suspicion was growing upon me and as it
grew, Fujita, looking at me somewhat quizzically, explained,
"Until not too long ago, *tattooing* was a common practice in
some groups of Japanese. When our anatomists saw beautifully
tattooed cadavers brought into the laboratory, it seemed proper
to remove and save the skins. So here they are, most of them with
the four extremities as well as the trunk." Although a long-time
anatomist, I shall admit to a slight crawling of the hair on the
back of my neck in thinking of the true nature of these beautiful
specimens! There were many specimens, including sections cut
through the entire body, some crosswise and some lengthwise,
preserved in formalin, a method of demonstration employed

to an increasing extent in recent years in our own laboratory in Indiana. There were also excellent wax models, chiefly from Europe. But one of the most striking objects to me was a complete human skeleton—made of wood! It had a very natural appearance, much more so, I thought, than some of the plastic ones made in our country. Another unusual specimen was the dissection of the heart of a whale, a huge thing, with the conduction system, which ramifies through the heart muscle, painted a vivid red.

In one case was an exhibit of burns and sudden death. My first surmise on these was correct—they were from Hiroshima!

From the museum we went to pay a brief visit to the laboratory of Doctor Hiroshi Hosokawa. His chief research theme was an interesting and unusual one—the histology of the nervous system of whales.

However, it was now time for the more formal part of my visit. My lecture was delivered under very favorable conditions, with excellent projection of the lantern slides. Dean Yoshida was present and entered into the discussion afterwards. Besides the strictly scientific questions which were touched upon, there was a bit of jesting from the dean. I had put on the board the figure of "twenty-six trillion," the estimated number of cells in the adult human body. Doctor Yoshida, acutely observant, pointed out that the first two numbers "2" and "6" multiplied by each other opportunely gave "12," the number of zeros which I had strung out after them!

A little social affair followed the lecture. In another building on the campus, the Faculty Club, we sat around a table well laden with Sapporo beer, from the northern island, Hokkaido, with platters of delicious little sandwiches and with salted peanuts. The conversation ranged widely. I learned that the university had about 10,000 students. The medical school, however, had only eighty to ninety per class (less than half the number in our class at Indiana University!). Actually, my friends told me, there is relatively little elimination by failure of medical students in Japan. This is due to the fact that admission is only by examination, and the examinations are very difficult indeed.

Of those who take them at Tokyo University, only about 20 per cent receive passing grades.

Our talk turned to languages and the subject of derivation of words in western and in oriental tongues. The importance of Sanskrit in the origin of most of the European languages was recalled, and somebody explained how the Imperial University had been given the valuable library of the great scholar of Sanskrit, Max Müller. He had felt a particular friendship toward Japanese scholars, with whom he had corresponded. Some had worked with him at Oxford.

In the Japanese schools, they told me, both of the syllabaries, Hiragana and Katakana, are taught; but they should not be mixed together. The Kanji characters, the beautiful calligraphy of China, also are studied. Now, in a six-year course, a Japanese student learns about a thousand of these; formerly he had to learn many more.

After an hour or so, we said our goodbyes and two of the younger faculty men drove me back to the hotel. It had been a day for me of a multitude of new and interesting impressions and the opportunity to become better acquainted with a fine Japanese scientist—Professor Tsunetaro Fujita!

* * *

Several days passed. We had returned from an eventful trip to Kyoto and Nara, and this morning we were to leave the city of Tokyo to fly to Hong Kong. A heavy rain was falling when we left the hotel in the airport limousine. It was only a little after six o'clock. In spite of the weather, we enjoyed this last view of the Tokyo streets, which by now seemed much more familiar to us.

We had not, while in Kyoto, been in touch with anyone in Tokyo, and while our friends had a general idea of our schedule, we expected no one at the airport to see us off on this early and rainy morning. But just as we entered the great foyer, there stood Professor Fujita. With true Japanese hospitality, he had remembered his guests and had come to bid us farewell—one added happy memory of our visit!

Chapter 14

GLACIAL WARMTH

A Visit to Doctor Fritz Verzár

BASEL lies at the junction of three countries: France, Germany, and Switzerland. It is one of the major Swiss cities, picturesquely situated on the high banks of the Rhine, which is already a large river at this point.

It was in Basel, I had learned, that an Institute of Experimental Gerontology had been established very recently. Its founder and first director was Professor Fritz Verzár.

Born in Budapest, Hungary, in 1886, Verzár had received his medical education in that country and had begun his scientific work in my own field of study, microscopic anatomy. He had worked under the renowned Hungarian histologist, Professor Lenhossek. The work of Lenhossek had included many studies on the microscopic structure of the nervous system and had ranged all the way from earthworm to man. Later, however, Verzár's interests shifted to more physiological ones, and he had studied with leaders in physiology in a number of laboratories. Since 1930 he had held the professorship of physiology at the University of Basel.

This summer, a Congress of the International Association of Gerontology, the fourth of its kind, was being held in northern Italy, at the little town of Merano. Professor Verzár's name was on the program. I looked forward to an initial contact with him there and later that summer, during a stay in Switzerland, to a visit to the new institute.

It was on the first workday of the Congress, at the Bristol Hotel, that I met Professor Verzár. In fact, we both had been

FIGURE 27   Fritz Verzár.

appointed to the Biological and Medical Research Committee of the Association. This was a really cosmopolitan group, which included Danielli of England (now of the United States), Verzár of Switzerland, Bourlière of France, Jalavisto of Finland and Shock, Kirk, Cowdry, Birren and myself of the United States.

The first meeting with Professor Verzár was brief and included only a formal introduction. Of average height, he was of more than average sturdiness, and the graveness of his mien, on this, a professional occasion, gave him an air of physical and mental solidity which still impresses me as one of his outstanding features.

There were several hundred participants in the Merano meeting, and during the next several days I had only an occasional glimpse of Professor Verzár. Once, at a reception, when he saw me with two cocktails (one was for my wife) his eyes twinkled, and he jested about my being "thirsty."

During a scientific session, where the subject was connective tissue and aging, Doctor Verzár gave an excellent review of the work in his field. His own work he described at this time only as a part of the broader perspective. He had been investigating the properties of *individual* connective tissue elements from rats of different ages. One of the difficulties in study of aging tissues has been that of being certain that the investigator has chosen *corresponding* units from the different individual animals. In the large connective tissue fibers from the tail of the rat, Professor Verzár had found material in which this difficulty was largely overcome. His studies included measurements particularly on the changing physical characteristics of these elements, such as the elasticity and the tensile strength. From the standpoint of an histologist, an attractive feature of the large fibers is a beautifully cross-striated appearance, seen with the light microscope.

I did not have an opportunity to talk with Professor Verzár in Merano after this meeting. I did, however, attend a meeting of our Biological and Research Committee at which he was elected chairman of its European division. The name of the tavern where this meeting was held would be difficult to forget —it was called the "Wunder Bar"! At this meeting I heard also a little about Verzár's studies on human subjects—longitudinal studies, i.e., investigations in which the physiological tests could be repeated on the same individuals between the ages, say, of sixty-five and seventy years. In these studies, employees of the great Swiss pharmaceutical company, Ciba of Basel, were serving as volunteer subjects.

From Merano we travelled by train to Venice for the two concluding days of the Congress. It was our first visit to that magnificent city, and every moment of our stay is memorable. So much has been written and said of Venice, but Gautier's lovely stanzas, beginning:

Sur une gamme chromatique
Le sien de perles ruisselent,
La Vénus de L'Adriatique
Sort de l'eau son corps rose at blanc

from his "Emeraux et Camées" have remained in my mind.

From Venice, we travelled, again by train, to Zürich. Our route took us through many historic and fascinating places, where we would have liked to linger: Padua, where Vesalius had been professor of anatomy; Verona, of the *Two Gentlemen;* Milan of La Scala Opera, then Como and Lugano with their beautiful glimpses of lake scenery. The long tunnels of the Gotthard Pass led us into Switzerland. When we emerged from the darkness, we saw snow on the high peaks and ridges.

As we approached our destination, we saw thousands of lights twinkling along the shores of Lake Zürich, and soon we were alighting at the great central Bahnhof of that city.

We found Zürich one of the most pleasant cities that we ever had encountered with its beautiful location on the lake with its traffic of little boats, the delightful groves and paths along the shore, the streets which looked as though they had been swept clean every morning (as a matter of fact, they *are washed* every night, not only by machine but by human hands), the old houses with bright geraniums in upper story window boxes and an air of peace and culture pervading the city. Our plan was to make this city our headquarters while we remained in Switzerland. This was to be during the greater part of the interim between the Merano meeting and the convening of the International Congress for Cell Biology at St. Andrews University in Scotland, a period of about three weeks.

We had rooms at the Neues Schloss, a very comfortable type of apartment hotel where we had a fine balcony. Since we took breakfast in the rooms, we had the balcony doors wide open, and usually a troop of busy feathered guests joined us for that morning meal, often feeding directly from our daughter's hand.

Soon after our arrival, I received an interesting letter from Doctor Verzár. For this part of the year he had gone to his high altitude laboratory at St. Moritz. He suggested that we come there to visit him for a few days and that later I could go to Basel to visit his other laboratory and to meet some of his colleagues and assistants there. I must admit that the idea of going to another part of Switzerland, and particularly to eastern Switzerland and the Grisons, appealed to us greatly, and in one sense we felt fortunate that Doctor Verzár was a two-laboratory man, even though I would not see him on my visit to Basel. So I wrote a letter of acceptance to his kind invitations to St. Moritz and to Basel and suggested dates for the visits. Thus we soon were preparing for our journey to St. Moritz.

On the day of our departure, the three of us were at the Bahnhof early. Provided with second-class coach tickets, we sought out the track for Chur and got aboard. The seats were plain wooden benches, but comfortable enough. We proceeded first along the shore of the Zürichsee, then to the Lintkanal which links the Lake of Zürich to the Walensee. Along the south shore of the Walensee we continued to Flums and so to Bad Ragaz. During this part of the trip we passed within a few miles of the little kingdom of Liechtenstein, one of the very few real monarchies left in the world. The gateway to the vast, mountainous region of the Grisons is the town of Chur. Many of its inhabitants still speak the ancient Romansch language.

At Chur we changed trains. Not far from here the two rivers known as the Vorderrhein and the Hinterrhein join to form the Rhine. Now we were following the Hinterrhein almost directly southward. Soon the whole landscape began to tilt upward, and at times our little train seemed to be following itself.

Strictly speaking, St. Moritz is not a city at all. It is a little village around whose health-giving baths and natural beauties there has developed one of Europe's most renowned resort areas. We knew that it had been called the playground of the world, that it had been the site of the Olympic Games in 1928 and that it had been used as a colorful setting for many motion pictures. We were a little surprised, therefore, although not unpleasantly so, at the quiet atmosphere of the station as we pulled in—but then it was in mid-summer.

Professor Verzár was awaiting us and greeted us warmly. "You are looking well," he said, "and right for a little vacation."

We drove through the streets of St. Moritz Dorf and over to
the National Hotel. Here we were introduced to the manager,
Fred Wyssl, a quiet-seeming individual who, we soon learned,
had been the hero of many dramatic rescues from the surrounding glaciers. He flew his own plane and this, indeed, fitted
with skis, was the instrument of rescue for, skillfully piloted, it
could land in seemingly inaccessible places.

Professor Verzár stayed at the hotel with us for a delightful
lunch which was brightened by some very fine white wine.
Afterwards, we walked over to the famous baths, for it was
in this area that the laboratories were located. We left my wife
and daughter strolling in the beautiful gardens of the Grand
Hotel des Bains, while we went over to the work areas. The
arrangements here were interestingly different, for the dormitory
room of each scientist was just across the hall from his (or her)
individual laboratory. A variety of studies was in progress. A
physical chemist was studying precipitation of various chemicals
from solutions and the "possible effect of interplanetary factors
upon this process," a subject which at the time sounded a little
"out of this world" but which was well suited to the high altitude—and, of course, it was in the fall of that very year that
Sputnik I soared into the heavens and made all extraplanetary
factors seem suddenly very much closer, indeed!

Another scientist was studying the protozoan Paramecium,
particularly in relation to the effects of various types of water
for its environment. Many dishes of culture were thriving, and
a bit of the fluid, held up to the light, showed immense numbers of the organisms as tiny white specks, just visible to the
naked eye, but swimming about actively.

Doctor Verzár showed me some graphs made from his own
studies here which concerned the physical nature of mountain
air. The records were on the nuclei of condensation in this air.
"My own workplace is in another building," he told me, "a very
old place which once was a bakery for the hotel." We went
over to the once-upon-a-time bakery, a building some hundred years old. Inside, however, were the paraphernalia of
modern science. Here, in a complicated apparatus, the air was

passed over water into a Wilson chamber. A galvanometer and a graphic recorder showed the amount of nebulosity present when condensation takes place. Doctor Verzár was particularly proud of some electromagnetic valves of very high quality used in this apparatus and manufactured in Aarau, a city a short way west of Zürich.

We stepped out of the laboratory into the clear mountain air. "Would you like to see a little of the Engadine yet today?" he asked. "We could take a drive over to Pontresina, and you could rest here afterwards." Actually, with the comfortable travelling, the magnificent scenery along the way and the stimulus of our greeting, we did not feel at all tired and said that we were quite ready for a drive.

Now we had an excellent chance to see the farmhouses of the Engadine, which were not like anything which we had seen before. Thick-walled, with small and deep-set windows, they are designed to protect their owners from the most severe winters, yet many decorative effects in carving lend them a gay and rather carefree aspect. There are wide doors for the cattle, leading into the first floor of the building where hay is stored and where the livestock pass the winter. We drove slowly through the little village of Pontresina.

Our automobile now was ascending steadily, and suddenly a beautiful vista opened out on our right—a fine view of a great glacier, the Morteratsch. The massive field of ice above us could be seen to be formed by the union of two arms which descended from a still greater height. We were close to the very edge of the glacier. We left the car and walked through the crisp, cool air over to where we could plunge our hands into an icy torrent which cascaded out from the ice sheet. We gathered a few of the marvellously smooth glacial rocks and pebbles, so similar to the ones which I picked up during walks on the shores of Lake Superior as a boy, evidence that great sheets of ice such as this had once covered much of our own country.

We were grateful to stop briefly at a little inn near the glacier and stand around the glowing stove. Here we met a family from

Amsterdam, the Grootes, who, like us, had been in Merano, and, like us, now were tourists in Switzerland!

We descended now and it was decided that we would drive over for a brief visit to Mrs. Verzár who was staying with her two children at an inn on the shores of the Lake of St. Moritz. Here the road became unsuitable for our automobile, and we hiked a half mile or so along the shore of the lake. Mrs. Verzár, whom we had the pleasure of having met at Merano, greeted us. The five of us took a table in the open air for tea and cakes. She was English, and her home had been at Horsham. Among other things of interest, she told us of her acquaintance with Doctor McDougall, the Scotch psychologist who had a very considerable influence in getting Doctor Rhine of Duke University started on his long series of studies of extrasensory perception.

By the time that Verzár and the four of us (Mrs. Verzár remained at the inn) started back along the lake, the sun had set, the air had cooled, and our walk was a very brisk one!

We drove back to the hotel in the gathering darkness. The warmth and light of its cozy interior were most welcome. So also was the excellent dinner. Professor Verzár remained with us, and we were joined by one of his assistants, a young lady who was preparing to leave soon for the States to work with Clive McCay, the famous nutritionist at Cornell who even then was extending the life span of his rats by dietary methods. At the table with us also were the Piccardis, friends of Verzár who were enjoying a stay at St. Moritz.

I was very much interested in hearing at this time about Professor Verzár's work in South America. The story of his decision was particularly interesting. Actually, the decision which he had made was *not* to go, with the idea that he was being a good husband in refusing an opportunity which would involve him in a trip to such a distant place. "Jean soon set me straight on that one," he said smiling. "She told me that the way to be a good husband was *to take* such wonderful opportunities when they come along."

It was in 1949 that he had gone to Bolivia and Peru for the

FIGURE 28 Herr Wyssl and the plane with which he had made many
gallant mountain rescues.

Coca Commission of the United Nations. "Coca-chewing was a particularly bad problem among the mine workers," he told me. "In those difficult mountainous regions the natives sometimes are able to bear terrific hardships with the aid of coca-leaf, but when abused it causes more problems than it solves." Another portion of Doctor Verzár's personal story that was brought out during dinner concerned his assignment to the offices of the FAO in Washington in 1948. Washington had been our home for several years, and when he spoke of the Longfellow statue on Connecticut Avenue, close to his place of work, and where I had walked so many times, it made distant places seem very near.

After dinner, we continued conversation in the bar, over coffee and kirsch. I cannot recall all of the topics, but I do remember that they included the biological effects of radiation, the mutations in germ cells and in somatic (body) cells, Darwin's writings, the evolution of the eye and, in the cave fishes, the peculiar degeneration of this organ after an auspicious beginning in the embryo fish. In relation to this latter subject, I did not know it at the time, but, within a year, I was to go as professor of anatomy to Indiana University where Professor Eigenmann had been the first to describe this developmental sequence, working among the limestone caves of southern Indiana.

Professor Verzár now said goodnight, and we went upstairs to find our way under the eiderdown covers.

* * *

We awoke next morning from an unusually sound sleep. After breakfast in the room, we went downstairs and chatted with Herr Wyssl until Doctor Verzár's arrival. Together we went over to the gardens of the Grand Hotel Bains. Here we each sampled some of the waters, which may indeed be beneficial but which did not recommend themselves very highly to the taste buds. In the gardens, we saw a couple approaching down one of the walks, and as they came nearer we recognized two good friends. They were Doctor and Mrs. S. Hirsch, whom we had visited three years before in Brussels! They were spending a few pleasant days at St. Moritz following a trip to Italy.

After a little talk with the Hirsches, whom Doctor Verzár also knew, we left them and began a drive into the Upper Engadine. As we drove along we passed several small but beautiful lakes: Lakes Campfer; Silvaplana, and Sils. As we ascended toward Maloggia, the uppermost limit of the Engadine, there was a very real sense of adventure—a crescendo, as though we were heading toward an end and a beginning. And then— suddenly—we were there—the edge of the world—a drop of a thousand meters! We got out of the car and walked over to the brink. Mists, gray and eerie, were rising and swirling. "This is the place," Doctor Verzár told us, "where, they say, the weather is made." We could believe readily that something was being brewed and created in those strange nebulous gray masses below us and about us.

This is the lowest of the various passes between Switzerland and Italy. The ascent on the Engadine side, which we had made, is a gentle one; but the descent to the Italian side, to the Val Bregaglia, is alarmingly abrupt.

It was pleasant to step into a little restaurant nearby for coffee and conversation. We soon were on the subject of the historic aspects of Basel, which are manifold. "It was in Basel that the first edition, the original *De Fabrica Corporis Humani* of Vesalius, was printed," our host told us, "but the marvellous plates for the book had been made in Venice. For your anatomical interest, I might tell you, too, that Basel has the distinction of being the first city in which a 'prepared' skeleton was set up, with the bones cleaned and assembled. Some of the soldiers of Napoleon—Russians, they say—took two small bones from it, but otherwise it is still in fine condition." It turned out that our host had these data so ready at hand because he himself had taken part in producing a beautiful memorial volume on Andreas Vesalius, published in Basel in 1952.

It was during our stop here also that I learned that Verzár had known that interesting and controversial figure, Eugen Steinach. It is perhaps not known to many, but Steinach, who, through his experiments on rejuvenation had been famous and even a bit notorious at a much earlier date, died on May 13, 1944, in Territch, Switzerland. Born in 1860, he had been professor of physiology in the German University in Prague (1895-1910), and then worked at the Research Institute of the Academy in Vienna until 1938. In that year, with the German invasion, he came to Switzerland. It was very interesting to me to find that Verzár felt that Steinach actually had been a good scientific worker and that his early studies on transplantation of gonads of guinea pigs had been of much stimulation and help to those investigators who went on to the actual isolation of the sex hormones. Steinach also had done substantial work on conduction of the impulse in sensory nerves and on the nerve supply of capillaries. "Actually," Doctor Verzár said, "much of his work on capillaries anticipated that done twenty years later by Krogh." There was a curious story about Steinach's great white Lipizzaner horse, which he often rode. It appeared that one of the old scientist's chief concerns was that this animal be treated well after his master's death. Unfortunately, Doctor Verzár did not know what had become of the animal.

Leaving the restaurant, we drove a short distance, then alighted and the four of us walked along a forest path, among low pine trees. This time we had no idea of where we were being guided, nor had we heard of the peculiar natural phenomenon which we were to see.

But now we saw the first of the strange geological formations. Just to one side of the path was a deep, well-like opening. As we peered over the edge, we saw that it went down about fifteen to twenty feet and that its sides were curiously spiralled. At the bottom were several large and remarkably smooth stones. Along the path and all about this area were many of these structures. They are called the "Mills of the Giants"—the *Marmittee dei Giganti* or, somewhat more prosaically, the "Glacier Mills" or *Gletschmühlen*. There were many of them in this region. Verzár told me that the geologists have calculated their age as anywhere from 15,000 to 100,000 years. They apparently were formed by the action of the Forno glacier, which once covered the entire lake district of the upper Engadine. I do not know whether similar structures are found in other glacial areas. We now came into a small clearing and there rose before us the ruins of a tall edifice. "This," Doctor Verzár told us, "is an ancient Roman watchtower." It was just on the edge of the great descent and must have commanded a magnificent view for the imperial sentries. We went inside and found it a hollow shell.

We drove back to the hotel where Doctor Verzár stayed with us for lunch. It had been a wonderful morning in the Engadine!

* * *

During the afternoon we made a trip on the cable railway, first up to Chantarella and then on to Corviglia, where we left the car for awhile. Here there were imposing views of several great peaks: the Piz di Palii; the Piz Nair, and the Piz Bernina. The open mountainside where we stood was covered with white thistles, and every now and then a robust brown marmot would be seen among them. On the return trip we alighted at Chantarella and walked the rest of the way. The route was along steep paths, then wider ways, past a waterfall, beside great hay barns and finally through a beautiful forest area which ended not far from the hotel.

We were to return to Zürich by train this evening. Doctor Verzár called to drive us and our light bags to the station. We knew that it would not be too long before, as fellow gerontologists, we would meet again. Still, it was not easy to say goodbye and to leave the warm hospitality of our host and the cool airs of the enchanted Engadine.

Chapter 15

THE WAY OF THE BUDDHA

A Visit to Doctor Banyen Davibhadhana in Bangkok, Thailand

IT WAS a night flight, a little over two hours, from Hong Kong to Bangkok. The evening had been unusually hot and sultry, and as I drove out to the airport with my wife and daughter, the streets were teeming with people. Although it was after 10 P.M., swarms of children were everywhere, while the grownups were carrying on their activities of buying and selling and barbering, and manufacturing a hundred kinds of articles—all in the open air. It was a fascinating scene, but the record heat in the city made the airport, with its air-conditioned restaurant, a welcome sight. We sipped tea until take-off time.

The lights seemed to fade away quickly as we left Hong Kong. We flew through the deep darkness over lands almost completely unfamiliar to us. Nor was there much to indicate a great city as we descended at the Bangkok airport. The lights seemed few and far between.

We had friends here, Thais with whom we had become acquainted in the States. First, there was Doctor Banyen Davibhadhana, with whom we had become acquainted in Cowdry's laboratory in St. Louis some nine years before and who had revisited the United States several times. Then there was Doctor Paka Srivanij, a charming young woman who had been a graduate student of ours at the Bowman Gray School of Medicine in Winston-Salem, North Carolina, four years before our present round the world trip.

Although our friends knew the date of arrival, I had not

FIGURE 29 Banyen Davibhadhana.

wired nor written to them from Hong Kong concerning the time. I felt that if I did, their hospitable natures would bring them out to the airport for our after-midnight arrival, and that would mean their being up half of the night. What was our surprise then, the moment we had cleared customs, to see our friends, accompanied by several other Thais, hurrying up to throw leis of fragrant tropical blossoms about our necks. It is a wonderful way of saying welcome! In a few moments we were in a private car. We sped along a road running across remarkably flat country. On either side was a row of trees and then lower-lying land from which a thousand night noises came to our ears. The ride to the city was over ten miles, but it was a rapid one.

Soon after we had entered the city streets, Doctor Banyen pointed out a great hotel which we were passing. "That is where Doctor Cowdry stays when in Bangkok. It is the Erewan." This hotel was of double interest to me, as being "Doctor Cowdry's," and as having a swimming pool, a real asset in the Tropics. I made a mental note of it for next time, but now we had to go on to The Oriental where our reservation had been made. Incidentally, *Erewan* is the Thai name for the figure of the triple elephant head, one facing forward, one to each side. It is like the national symbol of India, the threefold lion of the Asoka column, upon which the edicts of that great king were engraved, and also like the threefold human head, the Trimurti, found in the caves at Elephanta near Bombay.

The Oriental proved to be a very fine hotel. Our quarters were on the top floor and of a rather unusual style, a split-level arrangement with a living room below and the bedroom and bath above, reached by a little stairway and seeming like a balcony to the living room. But we were a little too tired on our arrival to notice many details, and it was only when the early morning light began to come in that we realized what a superb and really exotic view we now commanded.

❊ ❊ ❊

The windows of our living room looked out upon a broad river. Its brown waters, even at an early hour, were alive with activity. A dozen types of craft were plying up and down, their varied shapes and sizes presenting an ever-changing panorama. Among them were some of considerable size, loaded with freight, yet propelled and steered by a single long pole or oar.

Beyond the river, opposite to us, was an area of lush green jungle, extending as far as we could see and with only a few roofs appearing here and there among the trees. But off to our right was a magnificent sight. There, the morning sun shone upon sharp spires, great domes, and tiered pagodas. Bangkok is a city of temples. Our hotel actually was not far from the

center of the city, but the region just opposite us was that
peculiar one of the *klongs*, where all human habitations clustered
along canals within a veritable jungle. There was activity even
in the sky above us in this vista of ours. Strange vulturelike
birds, with brown bodies and dead-white heads, soared and
wheeled over the river and jungle.

What was this river? I had read something about the various
places where we were to stay, but somehow this had escaped
me. "Mekong" came to my mind, but this mighty stream is a
considerable distance to the east, flowing close to the ruins of
Angkor Wat in Cambodia and then emptying into the South
China Sea. At breakfast I learned from our waiter that this is
the Menam Chao Phya, which empties its brown flood into the
Gulf of Siam not far south of Bangkok. Well, after all, how
many of us Americans can go far on the origin, course or place
of emptying of even the mightiest of rivers in southern Asia—
the Indus, the Ganges or the Brahmaputra?

After breakfast we awaited the arrival of Doctor Sangvichien,
Professor of Anatomy at the Siriraj Medical School. This morning he was to take us to the Marble Temple, and later we would
meet Doctor Banyen. As we walked to Sangvichien's car, he was
saying, "The Marble Temple is noted for its many images of
the Buddha. You perhaps are acquainted chiefly with one way
only of portraying the Great Teacher."

As we drove through the streets behind our hotel, we saw
now a busy and rather modern city, but one very unlike those
of the West. Small shops were numerous. The crowds were
varied, and here and there the brilliant orange robe of a
Buddhist monk appeared.

We made the approach to the Temple on foot. The brightly
painted and gilded buildings were resplendent in the tropical
sun. Here were no ancient ruins but a vivid symbol of a living
faith, the religion of Buddhism which even now embraces over
150 million human beings in its tenets of the compassionate life.
On either side of the gateway stood huge guardian dogs, with
heads vaguely resembling those of lions. Within, ranged along
the temple buildings which surrounded a spacious courtyard,

were the images of the Buddha. Here is a figure with one hand
upraised, in admonition to cease from bickering and warring,
there a figure with both hands upraised, as the Buddha calms
the waves of the angry ocean, a third, seated but in a com-
manding position, subduing an enemy, *Mara*, a fourth, in an
attitude of teaching, and a fifth, in an attitude of meditation.
One striking figure showed the Buddha in an extremely emaci-
ated condition, seemingly not much more than a skeleton, with
the soft parts of the body shrunken against the bones. "From
an anatomical viewpoint," Doctor Sangvichien said, "the sculptor
here has done an interesting piece of work. In fact, I have had
a paper published on the anatomical aspects of this statue.
Let us go, now, into the sanctuary."

We left the brilliant sunlight to enter one of the temple
buildings. As our eyes became accustomed to the dimness of
the interior, we saw opposite us a tremendous golden figure of
the seated Buddha. Passing to and fro before it were the monks
clad in their orange robes. We approached more closely and
saw that before the main image was reached there were other
smaller but very interesting objects. One was the chair of the
priest, facing toward us and mounted on a small platform. The
other was a second image of the Buddha, golden, like the first,
but otherwise strikingly different from it. While the great image
had the characteristics which we are apt to associate with
an idol, the smaller image, at least in body, was that of a man.
Here, the thought of the Enlightened One as God dwelling in
the human frame was translated to us most impressively in this
exquisitely wrought statue.

From the temple we drove to the hospital where Doctor
Banyen was waiting. We two took leave of the others and went
on to his institute. The Chulalongkorn Medical Faculty or
School, somewhat confusingly, adjoins the Chulalongkorn University, but is not a part of it, nor is there any organizational
connection. Both, however, are named in honor of the great
king, Phra Paramendr Maha Chulalongkorn, who reigned from
1873 until 1910 and introduced many important changes. He
abolished slavery, simplified the amazingly complicated etiquette

of the court, erected schools and hospitals and established a standard postal and coinage system. For this capital city he instituted a lighting system, an improvement of sanitary conditions and an efficient police force. Many of his reforms and improvements can be traced to the fact that he, first among the monarchs of Siam, travelled abroad, to the Dutch East Indies and to India and later to Europe and that he appreciated and was able to make use of foreign ideas. He was a member of the Chakri dynasty known as "The Lords of Life," who already had ruled Siam since 1782. His father was King Maha Mongkut—actually known as Phrabat Somdetch Phra Paramendr Maha Mongkut Phra Chau Clau Chau Yu Hud! whose wise and progressive policy had opened the way for the great accomplishments of his son.

An impression from an early traveller, Mr. George B. Bacon, who visited Siam with the vessels of the United States East India Squadron in 1857 and was present at the ratification of our treaty with the Siamese, presents a vivid view of the Siamese Monarch at that time. He is speaking of his visit to the court of Maha Mongkut:

> . . . on his head he wore a cap or crown that fairly blazed with brilliant gems, some of them of great size and value. There was not wanting in his manner a good deal of natural dignity, although it was constrained and embarrassed. . . . He seemed burdened with the care of government and saddened with anxiety, as if he knew his share of the uneasiness of 'the head that wears a crown'.

He goes on to tell of the magnificent royal diamonds, great emeralds "of a more vivid green than the tropical foliage, and rubies and all various treasures" which the Indian mines afforded. It will make this ruler, his cares and his treasures, seem a little closer to us when one recalls that he is the king of *Anna and the King of Siam*. The "Anna" was a Mrs. Anna Leonowens, the English lady who had assumed a position as governess and teacher of his young children. From her accounts, it is well known that he was not without his share of faults, but the almost unlimited power and wealth of his position certainly would foster some indulgence. The remarkable thing is the wisdom

which he did display, his love of scholarship and his willing-
ness to accept new and foreign ideas.

* * *

The basic science departments of the Chulalongkorn Medical
School were housed in a new building, modern in its design.
The front was ornamental with a great bas-relief of scientific
activities. Here, a scientist was holding a fossil skull to which
part of a clod of earth still was adhering in the sculpture. There,
an anatomical dissection was going on, and in another part of
the relief were a compound microscope and embryos in different stages of development. As we stood looking at this
panorama, Doctor Banyen told me that he himself was the
author of this design, and that, in fact, he had planned and, to
a large extent, supervised the construction of the anatomical
laboratories, which were only a few years old.

We entered the building, which looked much like any well-
set-up western building designed for a similar purpose. On the
second floor was the laboratory of histology. Here a dozen or
so coeds were working. Their small size and delicate beauty
seemed well-suited to the investigation of microscopic objects,
and they were studiously concentrated on their work. Professor
Banyen introduced me to the group, and we talked for awhile
about the specimens. As we were leaving, several more Thai
coeds entered. They made the little prayerlike sign of greeting
which I now saw for the first time, but which I was to see so
often here and in India.

Banyen led me down the hall. "Here is our lecture room,"
he said, throwing open a door. "This also I had the opportunity
to design." It was a beautiful hall with excellent seating arrangements and, at the front, all of the facilities for projection,
drawing and other teaching aids which any lecturer could desire.

Now we ascended another flight of stairs to the laboratory of
gross anatomy. Banyen, as chairman of the department, is an
all-around anatomist and about equally interested in the various
subdivisions of his field. In the area of gross anatomy, much
interesting work, with cutting of large sections for study of different parts of the body, and with excellent injections of blood-

vessels, was going on. A beautiful specimen of a complete aortic arch, with its large branches for the arms and the neck and head, lay in a tray of formalin ready for further steps on its way to becoming an instructive museum specimen.

In the main student laboratory the arrangement of work tables offered ample light and room. "We use here the 'double dissection' method as instituted at Columbia University by Dudley Morton," Banyen told me. This was the method, I knew, in which the students did a general, rather superficial dissection of one body, then came back and carried out a more detailed dissection of a second one. Few schools in the States, however, had enough material available for such a method. Here Banyen introduced me to his assistant, Doctor Boonrug Kanjanapokin, who had spent some time at the University of Michigan with my friend, Russell Woodburne. Later Banyen told me, confidentially, "He is a fine anatomist, and I am training him now to be my successor." I could not help wondering whether this meant that a new post, perhaps in the government, was in the offing for Professor Banyen who now ushered me into his private office, the sanctum of the department. On the wall were pictures of colleagues, two of them being of the well-loved Cowdry. One of these was a huge, larger-than-life enlargement, and it was even a little startling to see this genial face shining out from a wall so far from home. Here, there were evidences of Banyen's own brilliant career, and it was not difficult to fall into a discussion of his studies and work. Chulalongkorn University had been his alma mater, and from her he had received his Bachelor of Medicine degree with highest honors—in fact, five different medals for excellence!

Banyen Davibhadhana was born on June 3, 1908, at Bangkoknoi, Dhonburi, Thailand. Beginning in 1914, he entered upon his formal education. He had two years in what is called primary school, four in high school and one in precollege work. He then entered the Chulalongkorn University Faculty of Arts and Sciences in 1924, or at the age of sixteen! After one year of work there, he entered the faculty of medicine, from which he graduated with the degree of Bachelor of Medicine in 1929.

Evidently his scholarship was highly regarded, as he was awarded "first honor," with the bronze medal in each of the four categories of pathology, medicine, surgery, and obstetrics and gynecology. In addition, he received the gold medal for the highest grade average in the total number of the medical courses.

At the early age of twenty-one, he entered upon his residency training, which he took in the Department of Obstetrics and Gynecology of the Siriraj Hospital. The residency took two years. In all of his conversation with me, I felt how strongly he held the idea of *self-education* and of continuing improvement throughout life—the idea of a path or a *way*. Life after the school days was not to him only a matter of work and of getting ahead professionally—it was an ever-continuing study. Yet, what a variety of positions he had held! And how amply had his practical achievements been recognized by the king and government of his country! He had worked for four years as a municipal health officer in one of the northeastern provinces of Thailand, organizing medical and nursing work and training. He had served for nearly ten years as surgeon at the Vajira Hospital in Bangkok. He became editor of the "Medical News" of the Thai Medical Alumni Club of Bangkok, and had written a *Textbook of Anatomy and Physiology for Nurses* which comprised two volumes and 1270 pages in the Thai version.

His surgical work ranged from gynecological to maxillo-facial, and in all kinds of surgery his keen knowledge of anatomy stood him in good stead. He had served in 1946 as deputy dean of the Faculty of Dentistry of the University of Medical Sciences of Bangkok and also as acting head of its combined Department of Bacteriology and Pathology. It was in 1947 that Doctor Banyen was appointed head of the department of anatomy. Perhaps the most interesting thing about this was the fact that no real department of anatomy of Chulalongkorn Hospital had yet been established! Banyen had to organize it, as he told me in rather picturesque English, "from the scratch"!

"It was just at this time," he said, looking up at the greatly enlarged picture of Cowdry, "that some very good fortune came to me, for the government gave me the wonderful op-

FIGURE 30   A hand-carved teakwood elephant from Bangkok, a product
of Thai National Industries. About one-third natural size.

portunity to go abroad to observe methods of organization and
of teaching in the medical schools of your great country. And,
of course, my particular good fortune was to select, as my headquarters in your country, Professor Cowdry's department at
Washington University."

I did not require any extended explanation as to *why* my
friend thought of this selection as fortunate—for I knew Cowdry
well, knew his breadth of vision, his warm feeling for international cooperation in science and knew how his very presence
seemed to boost the enthusiasm of others and often to throw light
in dark places.

"The term of my grant for visiting and studying abroad was
for two years and four months," Doctor Banyen said, "a very
generous one."

"You must have made very good use of it," I was prompted to reply. I was recalling how many American anatomists of my own acquaintance had taken occasion to mention to me some aspect of Banyen's visit to the United States. I remembered also that his research work with Cowdry had resulted in a publication on experimental skin cancer, published in the journal "Cancer Research."

"It was everything that I had hoped that it would be, and more," Banyen said. He told me how Cowdry had then encouraged him, along with his other activities, to take public speech training from the Tyro-Toastmaster Club of St. Louis. To me, this seemed very characteristic of Cowdry, with his vision of the role that visiting men such as Banyen would be likely to play in their own countries after their return. He told me also of a special honor received in Chicago—a diploma from the International College of Surgeons—a society esteemed by surgeons all over the world. The degree of Doctor of Philosophy in anatomy was granted to Banyen Davibhadhana by Washington University in 1951, and shortly afterwards he returned to Thailand.

In spite of the many accomplishments in his profession, Banyen had found time for a number of sports. As a child, he had loved kite-flying, fishing, swimming and diving. During his college days he had played chess, badminton, tennis (both lawn and table), squash, soccer and billiards. Then, too, he had developed a hobby of scientific photography. Later he had enjoyed riding, had served as tipper of horse racing and as honorary steward for horse racing of the Royal Turf Club of Thailand. He also had been captain of the well-known Nakorn Rajasima soccer team. In all of these activities, he has been an outstanding performer and a winner of important prizes. And lastly, he is no mean bridge player, having won seven cups for contract bridge in the tournaments of the Contract Bridge Association of Thailand, during the years 1944-1948!

I inquired of Banyen about some of the details of teaching at Chulalongkorn, failures, make-ups, honors and such matters that concern professors and students in any country. He showed me some of the records and what seemed to me a rather complicated but very well organized rating system. One thing which impressed me was how readily he could put his finger on *all* of the data concerning any particular student.

Professor Banyen's career since his return to Thailand had been marked by accomplishment and by distinction well recognized by his government. In 1952 he was appointed by royal decree to be a civil official of special class. In this same year he received the honorary M.D. degree of the University of the Medical Sciences. In 1954 he was given the great responsibility of designing and equipping of the new three story Anatomy Building, which his department now occupies.

In the following year he was sent to New Delhi, India, to the first All-Indian Medical Education Conference—a really historic meeting at which he served as representative of the Thai Medical Schools. Later, he was a member of the executive committee to organize the first Thai Medical Education Conference. This meeting was held at Bang-Saen, Cholburi, Thailand. From 1957 to 1960, he was a member of the security committee on the International College of Surgeons, Thai Section—the college into which he had been inducted in Chicago. In 1960 he was invited by the State Department of our country to spend sixty days here and to attend the Seventh International Anatomical Congress, which was held in New York City, in April of that year. Since 1957 he has been deputy dean of the Faculty of Medicine of Chulalongkorn Hospital and since 1958 a member of the Medical Act Committee of the Ministry of Public Health.

Among Doctor Banyen's outstanding surgical accomplishments is a special technique for repair or rejoining of the parts of the vas deferens after this tube has been interrupted, even for years. Vasectomy, the cutting of the tube, is a not uncommon operation in Thailand. In cases in which it is desirable for a woman not to bear children, for example, the husband often undergoes this operation. It was Banyen who showed for the first time that, when it seemed desirable, as it might in a remarriage, the tube could be reunited and serve once more as a

passage for the spermatozoa. Since his first attempt, he has repeated the procedure many times. Banyen reported the first
successful repair of vasectomy by end-to-end anastomosis in
1943. The report was made at a meeting of the Department of
Public Health in Bangkok.

We left the office, and Professor Banyen and I met my family
at the Golden Dragon restaurant for a very good and, to us,
unusual lunch.

✼ ✼ ✼

During our stay in Bangkok we did some of those things
which most visitors probably do. We took a boat along the
klongs, those canals which serve very much the same function as
streets, and which are almost inexpressibly colorful to the
westerner who never has seen anything of this type. The floating stores, with every kind of merchandise from pots and pans
to exotic tropical flowers, the neat, but lightly-built houses
along the bank, alternating with what seems to be little else than
tropical jungle, the occasional Buddhist temple set back a short
distance from the canal, with its graceful upcurved roof and
delicate spire and the groups of gay children swimming and
cavorting in the warm brown water were all parts of the unusual scene. It was peculiarly touching to see the little infants,
nude as the day they were born, waving at us from the shore
and greeting us with a happy "bye-bye."

Bangkok is a city of temples and palaces, and one could
spend months wandering among their splendors. One of the
greatest is the Wat Phra Kao, the Temple of the Emerald
Buddha. Actually, this is a collection of buildings rather than
a single one. Although it was begun in 1785, it was not considered complete until April 17, 1882, on the one hundreth
anniversary of Bangkok. It was King Chulalongkorn himself
who carried out the work of completion, at an enormous expense to his private purse.

When we entered the gateway of the extensive grounds, we
were struck by the seeming newness of everything. The marble
pavements, the brightly colored tiles, the ebony, mother-of-
pearl, and the gleaming brass and copper all seemed as though

freshly created for our visit. Huge and menacing figures, armed with heavy swords and with awesome tusks protruding from their jaws, stood guard. A short distance away there rose into the blue sky a great structure with a strange form—an erect, tapering tower surmounting a domelike base—the two somehow blending beautifully into an architectural form which we had not seen outside Thailand. Such a structure is called a *phrachedee*. In Buddhist countries of southern Asia, they are amazingly numerous. This one, however, is unique and, once seen, can never be forgotten, for it is the Golden Phrachedee. Its great mass is completely covered with gilt tiles, and the effect in the brilliant tropical sun is breathtaking. "I am sorry that there is not more time," Banyen said. "There are many shrines and things of beauty here, but perhaps we should visit the Obosot."

The Obosot, the true shrine of the Emerald Buddha, is the most holy of the structures in the entire compound of the Wat Phra Kao. Although it is not as impressive externally as some of the other shrines, those entering it immediately feel its great degree of sanctity. A tremendously high altar rears itself up from the dimly lit lower regions to heights in which the atmosphere is still more obscure. The altar is covered with a huge array of statues—bronze, silver and golden images of the Buddha —with vases filled with both real and artificial flowers, with tall, many-storied umbrellas, with European glassware reflecting the light of flickering tapers and with many other brilliant and varied subjects. Far, far above is the green jade figure, a statue of matchless beauty, found in 1436 at Kiang Hai and of unknown antiquity. This is the Holy of Holies—the Emerald Buddha.

☼   ☼   ☼

I have said a little about the distinctions which Professor Banyen Davibhadhana had received from his king, from his fellow doctors and from others in Thailand. These distinctions and awards and the occasions upon which they are presented are of great significance in the land of the Thais. Because of this, I shall enumerate the medals, the necklets and stars which he has received, adding, in some instances, a word of explanation.

Medals

1932—On the occasion of the inauguration of the King Rama I Memorial Bridge (yellowish green ribbon).

Rama I was the first monarch of the present line of Thai royalty and the founder of Bangkok. As "General" Chakri, he had distinguished himself in battles against the Burmese, and after a revolution in which King Taksin was deposed, he was called to head the state and become the first of the illustrious Chakri Dynasty, which remains in power to the present day.

1934—Merit for Service to the Thai Red Cross Institution (white ribbon clipped with Red Cross pin).

1943—Thai Royal Crown Medal of the Fourth Order (green ribbon).

1946—White Elephant Medal of the Fourth Order (red ribbon).

It has been said that if the elephant in Thailand is the king of beasts, the white elephant is the king of elephants. Actually, he is simply an albino animal, and his whiteness generally is in spots. He has been described as appearing often as of a faded pink or light mahogany color. The presence of one of these animals has long been thought to mean a pledge of prosperity to the king and country. In earlier days, they were treated with the greatest veneration, fed from vessels of gold and attended by numerous slaves. It is believed that albino elephants are found only in Thailand and in some of its previous dependencies, now neighboring states. A curious fact about this unusual creature is the existence in *Japan* of a day of festival for the white elephant. It seems probable that at one time there was a rather close intercourse between Japan and Siam. The flag of the kingdom, a white elephant on a red ground, attests the continued tradition of veneration, as indeed do the White Elephant Medal and Order.

1948—On the occasion of the coronation day of King Rama IX (orange stripes on the light yellow background ribbon).

1955—Medal of Honesty, Loyalty to H.M. the King of Thailand and Faithful Service to the Royal (Thai) Government over twenty-five years' duration (dark green ribbon).

1957—On the occasion of the anniversary of twenty-fifth century of Buddhist era (red and yellow ribbon).

Gautama Buddha was born about 620 B.C. on the borders of Nepal and died about 543 B.C. at Kusinagara in Oudh. While Buddhism originated in the Indian subcontinent, it was not destined to remain there in the flourishing condition seen now in Thailand and other countries of southeast Asia. A revival of Hinduism in India has left these other countries as shining examples of the Way of the Buddha.

Necklets

1951—Thai Royal Crown Necklet of the Third Order (necklet with green ribbon).

1953—White Elephant Necklet of the Third Order (necklet with red ribbon).

Stars

1956—Thai Royal Crown Star of the Second Order (star with necklet and green ribbon).

1957—White Elephant Star of the Second Order (star with necklet and red ribbon).

Sash

1960—Thai Royal Crown Sash of the First Order (green sash with Royal Crown medal and a star).

These are the external adornments, and very literally so in Thailand, of the distinguished type of career which Professor Banyen has had.

During our conversations, I asked him particularly about his sources of inspiration. "The early ones," he told me, "were, first, my beloved father, who guided my feet into the path of humanity by helping to mold my habits and behavior in such a way as to make them of the greatest possible good to others. Second, I was impressed greatly by the application and concentration of some cousins of mine who were studying law. Their example helped to guide me into the path of study. And third, some of my early teachers under whom I studied drawing and mathematics led me into the path of scientific and artistic endeavor. Since my school days, there have been several persons who have stood before me as real inspirations. Some of these have been very close to me, my own beloved father being one of them always. Others have been farther removed, as the father of our king, H.R.H. Prince Mahidol of Sonkla, whose wisdom and high-mindedness have been an inspiration to me for many years. On the clinical side, my early preceptor, Professor Carl Bachmann, stands out. Here in Thailand, Professor Chalerm Prommas has seemed like the ideal of a scientist and in your country, of course, my great friend and guide, Edmund V. Cowdry at Washington University. And last, but chief, of these personalities guiding my way," he concluded, "is my Lord Buddha."

At one point I asked him how he felt about the two aspects of his career—the active clinical work in which he had engaged, on the one hand, and the somewhat more deliberate academic activities of an anatomist, on the other. "I have enjoyed both of them greatly," he said, "and as I am sure that you know well, each contributes greatly to the other. Sometimes I have thought that the fundamental science, with its careful methods and its sorting and classification of facts, is more like bone tissue, while the art of medicine, with its constant need for flexibility and adaptation, for yielding to the conditions of the individual case, is more like cartilage tissue."

One afternoon toward the end of our stay in Bangkok, Doctor Banyen, my family and I went by launch to visit the Wat Arun, the Temple of the Dawn. This splendid structure was built by the Thai people as a token of thankfulness and reverence over 200 years ago when they reached this portion of the great river, after a southward journey. There had been fierce struggles with the Burmese in the north, and this portion of the land seemed like a peaceful haven. From the river, we ascended a few stone steps, and before us stood the Wat. A tremendous but graceful tower rises to a height of over 200 feet, its surface covered with ornamentation. A great carving of the Erewan, or three-sided elephant, looks out on the side facing the river.

It is surmounted by one of the gods of the Hindu pantheon. In the days when the temple was built, many of the features of Hinduism had come into this part of Asia. They were not necessarily in conflict with the Buddhist teachings, for Buddhism itself had arisen from that more ancient religion, somewhat as Christianity had arisen from the monotheistic religion of the Jews.

At the base of the great tower are four smaller structures or plans, as Doctor Banyen told us they are called. They bear beautiful figures in relief depicting four incidents in the life of the Buddha: first, his birth and infancy, with the seven miraculous steps which he made as a baby; second, the revelation which came to him as he sat under the Tree of Enlightenment; third, his first preaching to the Five, who became his ardent disciples, and fourth, his death, surrounded by his numerous devoted disciples.

I was surprised at the large numbers of excellent statues of Chinese origin—men, lions, a tiger with cubs and excellent horses. Most of the figures were life-size or larger. Banyen told us how close had been the ties between the Chinese and Thai peoples in the early days. In fact, the present location of the extensive grounds of the Royal Palace was once, before 1782, occupied almost wholly by Chinese, governed by their own administrator, a well-to-do Chinese merchant!

The Wat Arun was the last of the temples which we visited. I often think, however, of the very many beautiful places in Bangkok and in many other parts of Thailand which represent the devoted labor of thousands and millions of human beings over great periods of time. I am reminded then of the words of my good friend, Banyen Davibhadhana, "Where time is concerned, one hardly can find peace. True peace must mean a lack of the constant concern over time. The achievement which has brought to me the greatest satisfaction has been a gradual clearing of my own mind, a conquest over selfishness and petty goals, and the joy of doing things for humanity."

Chapter 16

KARACHI NOTEBOOK

A Visit to Doctor Mohammed Ishaq in Pakistan

I T WAS still well before dawn when the great plane landed at
Karachi, Pakistan. From London we had flown across Europe,
coming down at Frankfurt, Vienna and Istanbul. Flying low
over the domed mosques of Istanbul, we headed across the sea.

There was a striking view of the island of Cyprus spread out
below us, as on a relief map. We came down again at Beirut,
Lebanon, where I saw for the first time planes belonging to the
armed forces of the United Nations. From there it had been a
nonstop flight to Karachi.

Karachi! The very name had a sense of romance and exotic
interest to me. It seemed a strange and wonderful coincidence
that I should be coming here for a two-week visit. Indiana University, where I now was serving as professor of anatomy, had
established a Basic Medical Science Institute in this city, and,
under contract with the State Department, was carrying out a
program of graduate medical education for the doctors of
Pakistan.

The airport at this hour was not a very cheerful scene, for the
deep blackness of the surrounding countryside seemed to creep
close about the few lighted buildings. But for me there was a
welcome, and a warm one, which seemed to push the darkness
back. Carl Andreas, the young and vigorous administrative assistant of our Institute, was on hand to greet me and to drive me
into the city.

Along the dark road we talked about the Institute and about
the work of the next two weeks. Four of us from Indiana University were coming out to take part in a conference with

FIGURE 31 Mohammed Ishaq.

scientists and doctors from many parts of Pakistan. The timing was important, for the plan now was to begin to replace the American professors of the Institute with able and well-trained Pakistanis.

The streets of the outer part of Karachi were almost as dark as the countryside, but we soon pulled in to the high-walled enclosure of the staff house, run by the AID Division of our Department of State. Here the lights were burning, and an efficient staff was ready to receive visitors. My bags were carried to the second floor, and I was ushered into a large and comfortable room. Suddenly, the hot oppressive atmosphere of the streets was left behind—the room was air-conditioned!

I took time only to wash up and shave and then sank into a very sound sleep.

* * *

I was called next morning at 9:30, as I had asked to be, by a light rap on the door. I opened the heavy curtains over the windows. There were the roofs of Karachi. The buildings in this residential area were simple square or rectangular structures, most of them white but some in light pink or blue. They were surrounded by high walls behind which, from my vantage point, I could catch intriguing glimpses of gardens, with oleanders and other flowers. In general, the scene was not a verdant one and trees were represented mostly by a few limp palms. Overhead, in a clear blue sky, buzzards were wheeling.

I dressed and went downstairs. Here I was greeted by a Pakistani who obviously was in charge of the work of the porters, waiters, and other staff members. "I am Mr. Bakhsh," he said, with an interesting mingling of humility and pride in his voice, "the head bearer here." The term "head bearer" surprised me. I was carried back, for a moment at least, to the days of Curzon's India, to the "Lives of a Bengal Lancer," and to the thrilling beat of "Gunga Din." Of course, I suppose that the only bearing which Mr. Bakhsh now did was bearing down on his staff but, nevertheless, his title was a link to the past— and not such a very distant past, at that.

He showed me into a dining room, set to accommodate about a dozen persons, and I enjoyed a very American breakfast. I tried out one word of my scanty Urdu vocabulary on the man who had served me—*Shukriya* or "thank you" and was rewarded with a pleasant smile and an unintelligible phrase.

The staff house was a little over a mile from the Postgraduate Medical Center. A staff car, with driver, took me over some unpaved streets to the broader, paved avenue which led to it. Karachi, like most other cities of Asia, presents a scene of constant human activity. Men, women and children throng the streets, donkey carts clamor along, tall camels sway majestically past, and a great deal of motorized traffic, cars large and small, bicycles, and motorcycles, some of them rigged up as taxicabs, make the streets busy—and hazardous—places.

The institute had been established several years before. During the years of pioneer effort, its director had been Doctor Paul Nicoll, a professor of physiology from Indiana University. Actually, Paul had been born in what is now part of Pakistan, in the city of Rawalpindi. His parents were missionaries there, and the first seven years of his life were spent in that part of the world.

Karachi, the city where the institute had been built, is a bustling metropolis of over two million inhabitants. Here are some of the greatest contrasts between ancient and modern, between poverty and wealth, between primitive ignorance and enlightened foresight, which one can find anywhere in the world. Less than twenty years ago, Karachi was a quiet community, known to travellers by sea or air as a restful stopover. It had grown from a fishing village, on the shores of the Arabian Sea, to a prosperious and clean town, where the best elements of the native culture mingled with the more enlightened aspects of the British colonial system.

What had changed the town of Karachi into a sprawling metropolis? It was, of course, the great event of partition, which took place in 1947. Then the mighty subcontinent of Asia was in travail; and from that travail was born the new nation—Pakistan. Violence of the worst type—neighbor against neighbor —flared up in many places, and thousands upon thousands of Muslims fled across the borders of the new India into their own country of Pakistan. The revered leader, Muhammad Ali Jinnah, who had fought tirelessly for the establishment of this new nation, now rests in an honored grave high on a hill in Karachi. He died on September 11, 1948, having had but a short time to see his dream a reality.

Pakistan, geographically speaking, may seem to us in the United States a strange nation, for its east and west portions or "wings" are separated from one another by 1,100 miles of India. Yet we may remember that two great states of our own country—Alaska and Hawaii—are separated very widely from the rest of us. East Pakistan is much smaller in area, but has a much denser population than West Pakistan. It was West Pakistan, perhaps because of its more purely Muslim character, which became the seat of government. Karachi, the former fishing village, was now the capital of a country of over seventy million persons, some three-fifths of them living in East Pakistan.

Many of the refugees who flooded into Karachi at the time of partition had been compelled to leave most of their worldly possessions behind them. Only crude camps could be set up for these masses of people, and in the struggling new country it was to be a very long time before better accommodations could be obtained. Thus, the Karachi to which I had come was still a city in which primitive camps spread over many square blocks. Here what we would think of as the direst poverty existed along with real prosperity for some and lavish wealth for a few.

Our car pulled up at the doors of the Postgraduate Medical Center. The Center had been built for utility, not for display. It was a long one-story frame building. A hallway ran the length of the building, and from it double glass doors opened into the various departments. The central doors off of this hallway opened into the library, a room some seventy to eighty feet in length. A door at the left end of the library led into the lecture hall where the conference was to be held. In the library the group was gathering. Here I was greeted by the director, "our man in Pakistan," Doctor Harold Margulies. I had met Harold once before, during a visit which he had made to our medical campus in Indianapolis, just before he had gone out to Karachi. He was a man of somewhat less than average height, trimly built, with close-cropped black hair. Behind his glasses, his eyes were intense and, at times, a little hard. His features were fine and regular. More important, perhaps, than any aspect of his appearance was the aura of the man, a charged atmosphere of stored energy that made of him a sort of human Leyden jar. His field was internal medicine, and his ambitions were—great ones.

"Welcome to Karachi," he said warmly and grasped my hand.

"Did you sleep well?" I told him how really glad I was to have been invited to the conference and what a pleasant reception I had at the airport and staffhouse. In the next few moments I saw a number of other familiar faces. There was Doctor Donald Bowman, professor of biochemistry from Indianapolis, Doctor Alvin Levine of the department of microbiology, a scholar who had done much in the field of viruses and cancer and Doctor James Ashmore, professor of pharmacology. Bowman had flown over with Mrs. Bowman, coming by way of Europe. They planned, after the conference, to continue on through India, Thailand and Japan and so around the world. Levine and Ashmore were travelling together. They had flown from San Francisco and stopped briefly in Japan and Thailand. They planned, after the conference, to return by way of Europe. All of us were happy to see one another, but had little time to exchange greetings, for we soon were being introduced to a large number of the Pakistani participants.

The people of Pakistan are a varied group. In physiognomy they are not too unlike us, and in fact they share to a large extent in our own Aryan ancestry, being descendants of the early conquerors who descended upon the plains of the subcontinent from the great mountain ranges of the north. They were a nomadic, cattle-raising people whose original home is lost in the obscurity of the past. We know something of the greatness and imaginativeness of their minds from the magnificent poetry of the Vedas which was translated into English by Max Müller, the German scholar who made Oxford his place of work.

The professors and instructors whom we now were meeting were from all parts of West Pakistan and, some had travelled across India from the east wing. There was ample variety of appearance and complexion. I was impressed by the way in which their bright eyes and gleaming white teeth shown against the background of the rich brown of their skin.

We entered the lecture hall. There were almost one hundred persons gathered for this opening session. It was a rather brief one, with a welcoming and outlining talk by Doctor Margulies and a few words from an official of the government. At eleven o'clock we took a tea break, using the tables in the library and in another room. Margulies approached me. With him was a man whom I had not met earlier and whom he now introduced to me. "I would like you to meet Doctor Mohammed Ishaq," Margulies said. "He is the professor of anatomy at Liaquat Medical College in Hyderabad."

Ishaq held out his hand. He was a very fine-looking man, in early middle age, with a classical countenance and a neat, slightly gray mustache to set off his regular features. "I am most pleased to meet you," he said. His accent was that of one who not only had years of British education but surely had lived long in the British Isles. I felt instantly in rapport with him and thought to myself, "Here is a man whom I must come to know better."

I must confess that I was at first confused by the name "Hyderabad." I thought of it, as many Americans probably would, as the great Indian city where the Nizam, reputed to be the wealthiest man in the world, had ruled. That city, however, was very far away, on the Indian peninsula. The Hyderabad of Ishaq is, of course, Pakistani. Once upon a time it had been the capital of Sind, a native state. It lies close to the left bank of the Indus River. Hyderabad is built on the northern hills of the Ganga range. It was in a very strong natural position and had a fort which covered an area of thirty-six acres. The population is about 150,000, but after its surrender to the British in 1843, the capital had been transferred to Karachi. These facts I learned later, but they give us at least a sketchy picture of the city where Ishaq was living and working.

The morning tea period was over, and we filed back into the lecture hall for another hour and a half of talks and discussions.

One of the major topics taken up during the general sessions, and again in our smaller discussion groups, was that of medical school teaching and of the teacher student relationship. Professor Ishaq was one of the participants in the group to which I belonged, and in the conversation, as well as in personal discussions, I learned a good deal of his own philosophy on this subject. He emphasized the continuing importance of the teacher, as the most important "instrument" of all in the advancement of knowledge, even in this day of excellent visual and mechanical aids. It is on the teacher, Ishaq said, that the real responsibility rests for the insurance that there will be new teachers and new scholars as the stream of human history rolls on. It is for him to inculcate intellectual discipline in the future scientist and for him to be alert always to single out and encourage the young persons of promise—to fan the extra spark of intelligence and curiosity that it may grow into a bright flame.

It was of very great interest to me to find that Ishaq, with his educational training received in Pakistan and Great Britain, perceived and analyzed some of the recent trends in a way which accorded so closely with my own thinking. In the years of my teaching, I felt that I had perceived a tendency toward a decline not so much in the *status* as in the *role* of the teacher, which seemed to me to be an increasingly mechanical one.

Doctor Ishaq emphasized the need for the teacher to keep an open mind, to be trying always to learn and to be liberal toward his students in the imparting of knowledge. On the other hand, he said also, "The students should *take pride* in using the old expression, 'sitting at the feet of the teacher'—an expression which symbolizes the respect and even devotion of the learner toward his guide on the paths of knowledge."

It was during these first few days of the conference also that I learned about Ishaq's own educational background.

From an early age his thoughts had turned toward medicine and the laboratory. He told me once of a very early experience which I thought so graphically presented that I asked him to write it down for me. He has given it as follows:

> When I was six, I once accompanied my father to the medical college (at Lahore) to meet our family doctor—a lecturer in that college. There, while waiting for him, we stood in a laboratory. I watched everything around me with intense interest—the flickering blue flames, the glittering beakers and flasks and the white overalls—all this was new experience, first of its kind, leaving an indelible impression on my mind and one which to this day I vividly recollect. While stepping out to return home, my father, perhaps at the spur of the moment, made a remark to me, "How nice it would be if one day you became a professor in this college!" This sentence meant little to me at that time, but it became a part of the new experience.

The great influence of Mohammed Ishaq's early life came

from his father, who apparently had been a man of remarkable character and learning. Doctor Mohammed Iqbal was professor and head of the Department of Persian at the University of the Punjab in Lahore. Later he was also principal of the University Oriental College. He held the degrees of M.A. in Arabic from the Aligarh Muslim University and of Ph.D. from the University of Cambridge. The excellent record and accomplishments of Ishaq's father as a student led to his selection in 1918 as state scholar on an *All-India* basis to go abroad for higher studies. His thesis for the Ph.D., written entirely in the Persian language, was published in the famous E. J. W. Gibb Memorial Series. It was only the first of many publications.

He was a multilingual scholar, able to write and to speak English, French, German, Persian and Arabic, as well as Urdu. He possessed a fair knowledge of Hebrew. The personal library which he had collected consisted of about 3,000 volumes. They were in all of these languages and covered a wide range of subjects.

With the stimulation of such a father, it was perhaps not unnatural that three of his five sons obtained doctorates from foreign universities. One of the brothers is a physicist at the Massachusetts Institute of Technology, another is an orientalist at the Theological Seminary in Hartford, Connecticut.

But perhaps I have digressed too far in the description of the father. I did have at this time, however, during the course of my own stay in Pakistan, a very adequate reason to learn as much as possible about the family and educational background of Mohammed Ishaq, as well as about him as a man and as a scientist. The Institute at Karachi, a very important responsibility of Indiana University, was at a significant stage in its development, as we mentioned. From its first organization, in 1957, the professors and heads of the various departments had been American doctors selected by Indiana University from its own faculty or from faculties of other institutions in the United States. Thus, Doctor Bernstorf, professor of anatomy, had come from Hahnemann Medical College; Doctor Michael, professor of pathology, was from the University of South Dakota, and Doctor Minton,

FIGURE 32 Worshippers at a mosque in Karachi, Pakistan.

professor of microbiology, was from our own Indiana University
School of Medicine. The important change which now was to
begin was the gradual release of these American professors, to
return to the United States, and the appointment of Pakistani
scientists as heads of the various departments. As professor of

anatomy and chairman of that department at Indiana University, I was being asked to advise on the corresponding appointment for the Institute. Mohammed Ishaq was high on the list of candidates. Thus it was that I tried to learn as much as possible of his education and training.

One of the things which would seem strange to us westerners was the fact that his education, until the age of eleven, was entirely under the direction of his father. It included much stress on languages, particularly Arabic, but extended through many subjects and gave Ishaq a very good basis in mathematics.

Science, in the laboratory sense of the word, had to wait for formal school. We have had a glimpse, however, of one preschool incident, the visit to the medical college at the age of six, which left such a lasting impression. When, at eleven, Mohammed found himself a student in the laboratories of chemistry and of physics, he felt a great enthusiasm for these subjects and a deep devotion to his teacher of science—a Mr. B. Lall, whose meticulous appearance, kindness and attention toward his pupils, and stimulating personality he remembers even now with great vividness.

With a fine record in his earlier studies, Mohammed Ishaq was admitted to medical school. As in our own country, admission to medical school was something of which to be proud, but the honor was somewhat more marked, for there was but one medical college in the great province of the Punjab. His father, while not wanting his son to become too prideful, yet expressed his own gratification by permitting his son to buy any number of books and saw to it also that he was provided with a microtome for cutting thin sections of tissues, a microscope and a very fine set of microscopic slides, with sectioned and stained tissues for study.

❊ ❊ ❊

My conversations with Ishaq were carried on at odd times during the active and varied days of our conference. The sessions themselves had a number of features different from those of any meetings which I previously had attended. The native participants were devout Muslims, and the meeting would be opened by a reading from the Holy Koran, intoned by a *mullah*, a "learned priest." Some of these readings, as translated, sounded very familiar and could have emanated from the pulpit of my own Methodist church in Indianapolis. One, for example, was:

> Glorify God, therefore, when ye reach the evening, and when ye rise at morn:
> And to Him be praise in the Heavens and on the Earth; and at twilight, and when ye rest at noon.

I had brought with me to Pakistan a copy of the Koran, and late in the evening, in my air-conditioned room at the staffhouse, I greatly enjoyed finding the *Sura*, or book from which the verses had been taken and being able to see them in their context.

High government officials attended a number of our sessions. Brigadier M. S. Haq, Director General of Health Activities for the entire nation, spoke to us. Between sessions and at tea, which was served twice a day, I was becoming acquainted with faculty members of several of the medical schools of Pakistan. One of these was Doctor Wahid, Professor of Anatomy at Dow Medical College in Karachi. He had spent six days on the campus of Indiana University Medical Center and had studied for some months with Professor William Gardner, Chairman of Anatomy at Yale University. He, like Ishaq, was an excellent and enthusiastic teacher. It was interesting, however, to see the really great contrast in aspect and attitude between him and Ishaq. Wahid was short and sturdy, with a very dark complexion. He was extremely animated. Ishaq was tall, well-built but of much slighter form, with a light, almost white complexion and with an air of quiet dignity that seldom altered.

In talking informally with various Pakistanis, I learned that many of the names correspond in an odd way with those from our scriptures. Thus, "Yunus" is equivalent to "Jonas," "Yusuf" to "Joseph" and "Ishaq" to "Isaac."

I learned also that the Urdu script, which to the unpracticed eye looks a good deal like Arabic, is really a mixture of Persian and Arabic writing. It is a language which developed in the turbulent times of Mohammedan conquest and has been called the "language of the camp," as it was a means of communication among fighting men of diverse origins. Thus many words in it and in spoken Hindi are identical.

Our evenings were well taken up with receptions and entertainments of various types. One of these is especially memorable. It was at the home of Doctor and Mrs. Margulies and turned out to be a partly outdoor and partly indoor party. As we drove down the street leading to the house, we saw that it was no ordinary affair, for uniformed members of the Karachi police force were very much in evidence in the entire block. We left the car at the wide entrance to the yard and gardens. It was just at dusk, and the plants and varied blossoms bordering the spacious lawn helped to make a beautiful setting for the first portion of the party. The house was a very ample two-story edifice, and we were not surprised to hear that the Margulies occupied only the second story. The first belonged to a Mr. Grimes, an education director, also from the States.

Mrs. Margulies, our hostess, detached herself from a small group of guests and came across the lawn to greet us. She was a lovely person, beautiful, vibrant with life, tanned by the tropical sun and looking the picture of health. A little later that evening, I learned that her temperature that very afternoon had reached 101° and that she had gotten up from bed just for the party—but such is life in the Tropics!

"I want you to meet a particular friend of ours," she said to Professor Bowman and me. She led us over to another group and to a man who at the moment was in animated conversation. As he turned toward us, I was quickly, deeply and not too favorably impressed. "I would like you to meet Basheer Ahmed. He is the police chief of the Karachi district," Mrs. Margulies was saying. Basheer was a man of medium height and of solid athletic build. He had spent over twenty years on the northwest frontier, serving there also as a police officer. He looked to me as though he might have been hewn, and not too finely so, from the rock of the Himalayas.

The northwest frontier is the country of story and poem, the land that recalls to us "Barrack Room Ballads," "Plain Tales from the Hills" and "The Man Who Would Be King". It is the country of the Pathans, a proud, fierce race of hillmen, consisting of many tribes, to whom combat is a way of life. One remembers Kipling's "Lament of the Border Cattle Thief" and the defiance of the prisoner dreaming of when he will be free again.

'Tis war, red war, I'll give you then,
War till my sinews fail;
For the wrong you have done to a chief of men,
And a thief of the Zukka Kheyl.

Many years in that wild frontier region were a good background for his present work, for Karachi, with its mixed population, its refugee camps, its dark streets and its poverty, offered ample work for such a man. We heard, too, from various sources, that his methods were not gentle ones.

Later Doctor Margulies came over and introduced us to the High Commissioner for Canada, the representative from Morocco and the newly arrived ambassador of Algeria. We were still on our first scotch and soda, when we felt a few drops of rain. The shower quickly became heavier, and word went around that the party would be continued inside. It was interesting enough to visit the well-appointed and tastefully furnished quarters of Doctor and Mrs. Margulies; but a very large number of slightly damp persons crowded into a small area was not as pleasant as a lawn party, and the evening was somewhat shortened. Meanwhile, however, another event had occurred and was a topic of conversation among some of the guests. A rather large amount of the liquor for the party had disappeared, and rumor had it that some of the bearers had been passing cases and bottles over the wall to some friends on the outside—and this with the chief of police on hand! I could not help feeling sorry for any "thieves of the Zukka Kheyl" who may have been caught that evening.

The next few days of the symposium were busy ones. Each of us from Indiana University was presenting several formal lectures, followed always by free discussions in which our Pakistani colleagues were very active. Actually, I had to confess that I myself was learning here in Karachi more about the interests and work of my own colleagues than I had in many months in Indiana! Professor Bowman, our biochemist, presented an excellent paper on "Cation and Anion Balance," bringing in the clinical as well as the fundamental aspects. Doctor Ashmore spoke on "The Role of Enzymes in Homeostasis," a consideration of the role of these mysterious protein catalysts in maintaining the *status quo* of the body. He also participated with Doctor Salimuzzaman Siddiqui, Chairman of the Council of Scientific and Industrial Research of Pakistan, and with Doctor S.M.A. Zaidi, Professor of Pharmacology of Liaquat Medical College (Doctor Ishaq's school), in a session on "Antidiabetic Compounds." In this session I heard for the first time something about the dispute as to whether natural or "crude" drugs, as prepared in many parts of the subcontinent, might be actually more efficacious than some of the highly purified ones.

Doctor Alvin Levine gave a talk on "Recent Developments in Virology," an excellent presentation, which was supplemented by motion pictures, in one of which our great California virologist Wendell Stanley, spoke directly, as it were, to this audience in far-off Karachi. It was he who had carried out such a large amount of work on the tobacco mosaic virus and its chemical and genetic characteristics.

My own lectures were "The Study of Comparative Histology and its Value in Understanding the Human Body" and "The Role of the Junior Staff and Graduate Students in Medical Teaching, with Comments on Procedures." Since two of the graduate students who were very active in teaching in our own department in Indiana were from Pakistan and soon would return here, this latter discussion aroused a good deal of interest. Here Doctor Ishaq contributed a number of points and pertinent comments. Another of my responsibilities in the symposium was to lead a panel discussion on "Aging and Chronic Diseases." This, too, was a lively enough session, although I couldn't help feeling that the topic itself was not too appropriate, in a country where mortality was so heavy among infants and children.

There was hardly an evening when we were not invited to some official gathering or to a party at the home of one or another of the faculty of the Institute. One evening, about a week after the beginning of the symposium, it seemed as though there was not to be any invitation. I had begun to look forward to a few quiet hours with a book on *The Life of Beethoven* which I bought in New York just before leaving. I wrote a few post cards and went down to dinner. Only a few persons were in the dining room but I was having an interesting conversation with a Mr. Katashi Nose, an engineer from Hawaii who was helping to set up a technical training school in Karachi. Professor and Mrs. Bowman arrived and sat at our table—and there went the quiet evening! They told me that they and I were invited by the Mintons to go along to "see the turtles" at high tide. Minton, the professor of microbiology and one of our own Hoosier exports, was the best versed of all the faculty in the fauna of Pakistan and already had shown us his fine collection of nonpoisonous and poisonous snakes at the laboratory. While I really did not know too well what "seeing the turtles" involved, I was not about to miss the chance.

So it was that shortly after dinner the Mintons drove up to the gate of the staffhouse in their jeep, and the three of us climbed in. Soon we had gone through the busier parts of the city and were driving along the harbor area where the night seemed to become darker and the roads more lonely as we went along. As we came to some very low country, we saw a sign which said "Diversion"—this meant "detour." The water was too high. "This detour," Doctor Minton said, "will take us close to one of the large refugee areas."

In a few moments we were driving along a dark and dreary road. On one side were the waters of an estuary of the harbor. On the other were closely packed huts and hovels of thousands of refugee families. A dark figure would loom suddenly in front of us, or a group of children would scurry to the side of the road. The jeep slowed, for this was dangerous driving. It was, indeed, dangerous not only for the refugees on foot but for us in the car. An injured child in these circumstances can arouse the passions very quickly, and we had heard of instances where "justice" came very quickly to a careless driver, at the site of the accident. Fortunately, we did get past the camp without complications. As we turned onto a wider road, we saw more light ahead, and soon we were passing through the Sind industrial district, where large factories stood back from the road, and many little shops and eating places were still open. It was curious to see camels swaying along the street in such a factory atmosphere.

Now this well-lighted district was left behind, and the road became more and more a lonely one, passing over very flat, low country, reed-covered and swampy on either side. Suddenly there was a slight rise in front of us, and a row of beach houses silhouetted against the sky. We were at Hawks' Bay.

Taking the portable lanterns, we left the jeep and went up between the beach houses, all of which were silent and dark. Just as we reached the top of the rise, we saw before us our goal. The long, wide beach was a fairy scene. A great round moon lighted the sands, and beyond them were the swelling breakers with their crests breaking into a silver foam. This was the Arabian Sea! We all stood there for a few moments. The Mintons seemed to be almost as much impressed as were we, their visitors. The place was absolutely without sign of human life, except for the silent houses on the rise where we were.

We walked out onto the beach. In a few moments there were exclamations. The tracks of the turtles had been sighted. Then, almost immediately, we saw our first one. She already had dragged her heavy body over a hundred feet from the water and was engaged busily, with all four flippers, in digging a great hole. We were almost holding our breath as we approached her, but Minton said in a calm and not too low vioce, "Don't worry about disturbing her. She is so occupied with her own interests just now that if we are just a little quiet, there is no danger." He was right, of course, and we watched her for about ten minutes, then we went on down the beach.

Our next turtle was in an ideal place, near to some stairs leading up to a beach house, where we could sit down at leisure. She also was at an ideal stage in her task. The great initial hole was complete, and now she was using her hind flippers only, digging the true egghole. Even this process takes some time, and I wandered around a little with my lantern, picking up bits of shell, cuttlebone and driftwood. I saw Doctor Minton motion and came quickly back. The giant turtle had begun to lay!

He held up one of her hind flippers. One at a time, in orderly succession, the eggs appeared. They were like great, shining pearls, almost perfect spheres several inches in diameter. As each one emerged, it dropped the short distance to the bottom of the egghole. We took turns holding up the flipper, gently enough to be sure, but throughout the process our turtle "hostess," seemed to pay no attention to us whatever. We counted the great pearls as they were laid. The total was 120!

As the new mother began to fill in the egghole, we arose from the sand and began to gather up our things. What an experience it had been! And what a setting—with the moonlight washing over the long beach and the rolling surf of the Arabian Sea! Years ago, in English class, I had been thrilled by the little essay, "Turtle Eggs for Agassiz," by D. L. Sharp. Here in Pakistan were turtles and turtle eggs on a grand scale!

We were just about to start back when out of the darkness there appeared two men. They were *chokudors*, "watchmen," for this part of the beach. We exchanged greetings, and Doctor Minton talked with them briefly in Urdu.

It may seem strange that the giant turtles, potential source of so much fine soup and meat, go unmolested in this land where thousands are hungry. In this area, of course, the *chokudors* would be one answer, but a more potent one is a religious feeling against doing any violence to these creatures.

* * *

Meanwhile, my acquaintance with Professor Ishaq was becoming a firm friendship. We had a number of opportunities to discuss his work, his interests and his ambitions for the future. He told me how, soon after graduation from medical school, he had been assigned as house surgeon to Lieutenant Colonel A. Sargood Fry, Professor of Operative Surgery at Mayo Hospital in Lahore. Fry was a great disciplinarian with untiring devotion to duty, to his students and to the patients under his care. Ishaq told me one interesting story illustrating his attitude which I may repeat here:

One late afternoon, at the end of a day's work, as Doctors Fry and Ishaq stepped out of the ward, they found a messenger waiting—a tall, turbaned, smartly dressed figure in a scarlet uniform richly embroidered with gold. He bowed. With dignified reverence he held out a golden tray on which was a letter to Colonel Fry. For a moment, Fry stood in surprise, then took the letter and read it. It was a request from a *maharaja* to come and examine a patient, some hundred miles away. Outside, the Rolls Royce of the maharaja was waiting, and there was the promise to bring the Doctor back to Lahore by midnight—also the implied promise of a fine reward. Well, Fry had a lecture to prepare that evening—he declined to go! Instead, he sent an assistant, whom the maharaja did reward generously. Had Colonel Fry himself gone, he certainly would have returned a much richer man, perhaps he would even have brought the gold tray back with him!

Ishaq's association with Colonel Fry made him determine on surgery and further study as his goal. To go abroad for higher training would be the logical plan, but the war was on, and this was impossible. When the war ended, he entered the Department of Anatomy at Lahore as a postgraduate for a four month course. "Here I came under a really fine teacher," he told me, "Professor M.A.H. Siddiqui, who was a Fellow of the Royal College of Surgeons. He had a degree of Master of Arts in anatomy from the University of Toronto. At the blackboard he was an artist and he 'drew' almost every sentence which he spoke, really making anatomy come to life." Siddiqui took Ishaq on as a demonstrator (instructor). He assisted also in Siddiqui's experimental studies on the lungs of dogs. Indeed, he began a project of study for an M.S. thesis in this field, but soon realized the inadequacy of the research facilities available to him. It was then that he decided that the next step in his career must be to go abroad to study, even though no scholarship was available at the time, and he would have to go at his own expense.

For many years, the Royal College of Surgeons of the United Kingdom has given courses for doctors from abroad, and it was to pursue such a course that Ishaq first went to Edinburgh. Sometimes a bold step and a heavy expenditure seem to pay off. At least, it was while he was in Edinburgh and so engaged that word came to Ishaq from the Government of Pakistan that he had been awarded a scholarship for study abroad.

In the meantime, he had made a very significant contact, for he had attended several lectures by the great Edinburgh anatomist, Professor J. C. Brash, and had been impressed deeply by the learned and enthusiastic nature of his teaching. He talked with Professor Brash and was accepted by him readily as a research scholar for a Ph.D. degree. The topic of his study was to be the comparative anatomy of the lungs. Of much additional help in this relation was his second supervisor, Professor T. Grahame of the Veterinary and Comparative Anatomy Department of the University of Edinburgh. Grahame is the author of a classic, *Anatomy of the Dog*, a book of immense value in experimental medicine and surgery.

It is hardly surprising that, as Ishaq told me frankly, it was his work at Edinburgh that had given him most satisfaction and the greatest sense of lasting achievement of all of the enterprises which he had undertaken. It has been my own experience to note with what pride and really nostalgic pleasure many scientists look back to those days when study and research were almost uninterrupted and when the guidance and even friendship of great and learned men were within easy reach.

It is the custom, and indeed a necessity, for any citizen of Pakistan who receives his degree abroad to obtain a letter of recommendation, a "To whom it may concern" to present when applying for an academic post in his native country. In looking over Mohammed Ishaq's papers, I found two such letters, one from Grahame and one from Brash. Here is a part of what Grahame said:

> I found Doctor Ishaq a man of high intelligence with a quick perception, determination and great powers of concentration. The meticulous work he did and the manner in which it was undertaken is a testimony to his exceptional capabilities as a research worker. The methods

and the casts he made of the bronchial tree of the many animals were
the work of an artist. These works will be ever on exhibition in our
museum which is a further tribute to his skill. The monumental thesis
he wrote will stand as a work of reference to anyone interested in the
pulmonary tissues . . .

The letter of Brash is an unusually warm one. For instance, he
writes of Ishaq: "His friendly disposition obtained the good will
of all with whom he came in contact while working in my department, and I would add, if not irrelevant, that my wife and I
greatly enjoyed our social contacts with Doctor Ishaq and his
charming wife, being privileged to see something of their
family life during their stay in Edinburgh."

Of Ishaq's research work, Brash has this to say:

> Doctor Ishaq's thesis was a massive work containing impressive
> evidence of diligent and extensive study and of personal investigation
> of the general problems of bronchial distribution on original lines.
> The thesis was entitled *A Comparative Study of the Broncho-Pulmonary
> Segments and Pulmonary Blood-Vessels with special reference to the
> Dog,* and its principal part was concerned with the arrangements of
> these structures in that animal. It was splendidly illustrated by drawings
> and photographs, and indeed constituted a complete atlas of the pul-
> monary anatomy of the dog. It was so complete that it is difficult to
> see how anything can be added to work which is largely new. Many
> of the illustrations are photographs of the very beautiful corrosion
> preparations made by Doctor Ishaq—single, double and triple casts of
> bronchi and pulmonary vessels—which have been deposited in the
> Anatomical Museum of the University of Edinburgh, to the admiration
> of all beholders.

Such words are particularly weighty, as they come from Doctor Brash, as emeritus professor of anatomy at the University
of Edinburgh and long-time editor of the classical *Cunningham's
Textbook of Anatomy,* which, with the accompanying *Manual
of Dissection* in three small, but very weighty volumes, is
known to anatomists over the world. His degrees and other honors are numerous. Written out fully, his designation is "J. C.
Brash, M.C., M.A., M.D., D.Sc., LL.D., F.R.C.S. Ed., F.R.S.E."!

It is appropriate to point out here the very real difference in
the course and high points of a career in the medical sciences
for a citizen of a new or developing country and a citizen of,
say, the United States. The approach to medical science in
Pakistan and India naturally has been influenced profoundly by

the British tradition and method. Hence, the medical scientist must become, first, a medical man, must obtain a degree of Doctor of Medicine and have practical work in the hospital. This means that a man usually is mature and tempered before his research work and much of his specialized scientific training get under way. So it had been with Ishaq. Then, too, the experience of carrying out of the research and the writing, a report of it in a thorough and painstaking way, is a different type of experience from that of the American student. The opportunity to go abroad, to study under men like Grahame and Brash, is considered as a very real privilege and one which will affect profoundly the whole life and career of the student. While the process, both for a citizen of Pakistan and of the United States, would be described as "obtaining the Ph.D." in a basic medical science, its overtones and, indeed, its whole significance, are vastly different.

I was very much interested in Ishaq's philosophy of teaching. He had published a paper "Teaching of Anatomy" in the "Liaquat Medical College Magazine" with some considerations which seemed to me very important. I did not agree with all of his conclusions, but they certainly represented a thoughtful and a progressive approach. In order that we might discuss some of the pros and cons of the methodology, I invited him to luncheon at the AID staffhouse.

On that day only a few other persons were in the little air-conditioned dining room. The menu, however, turned out to be particularly good—"steak and chips." In the informal atmosphere, Doctor Ishaq told me a number of things which I had not heard before.

"It was an adjustment," he said, "returning after four years in Scotland—and there have been some frustrations, especially in finding time for research work. In my first position, at Nishtar Medical College in Multan, I was involved pretty deeply in construction planning . . ." I knew very well what he meant on this score. In several schools I had spent many hours in poring over blueprints and sitting in on conferences about new buildings or remodelling of old ones—a stimulating activity, but one in which the details often seemed to be endless. "In my present position at Liaquat Medical College," he said, "the administrative assignments are hardly ideal. For example, while professor of anatomy, I have spent a very great deal of time on another task—I was placed in charge of transport for the school. Since we are some miles out of the actual city of Hyderabad, this job is a big one." He expressed the highest regard for the general administrative work of the government and for the President, Ayub Khan. He did say, however, "It is only too true, though, that many of the administrators in the lower echelons have a very meager understanding of academic problems and needs."

I asked him about budgets at his medical school. He smiled somewhat quizzically, then replied, "Well, a chairman of a department here has no funds to handle." He looked at his fork. "If I need a fork, for example, I must write a letter requesting one. Money is not easy to come by. For the past several years I have been in charge of the contest for the 'best dissection of the year.' This year it has been cancelled, as there is no money to support it."

I found that many of the views of Ishaq, and some of the programs which he had been active in forwarding, were similar to my own. He was fighting against the strangling compartmentalization of the basic medical sciences, trying to bring anatomy and physiology closer together, attempting to have more living and applied anatomy taught throughout the years of medical school, and replacing rote learning with dynamic demonstrations, using fresh specimens from deliveries, autopsies, x-ray studies and other sources. At the Liaquat Medical School, regular combined teaching in the form of conferences of the whole staff and the clinical students had been instituted. At these conferences each professor would give a presentation of a clinical subject or case, primarily from the point of view of his own specialty, with all of the others contributing from their specialties, to the general discussion.

On the personal side, I learned the interesting fact that Ishaq's brother-in-law was a well-known actor and was at that time appearing in E. M. Forster's *A Passage to India* in New York.

That afternoon at the Institute I held a series of conferences with the graduate students who had carried out their training at various medical schools in Pakistan.

* * *

The vast subcontinent of Asia, which holds the lands of India and Pakistan, West and East, is at present a strange and at times astonishing, mélange of the most ancient customs and superstitions with the progressive and enlightened views, as we like to think them, of the modern world. An evening trip with some friends to an ancient shrine not far from the city of Karachi was enough to impress this very forcibly on my mind.

I went with Doctor and Mrs. Minton, and their daughter, together with a Mrs. Hoyle and her daughter. We used Doctor Hoyle's car, a beautiful air-conditioned machine. As we reached the coastal road, the lights and noise of Karachi faded behind us. We sped along not far from the water, then turned off onto a still darker way. As we ascended a hill, a glow of light appeared. Soon we were in the midst of a really motley throng of people. Strange sights, sounds and fragrances were everywhere. We stopped the car—we had to—it could not move forward amid that mass of humanity. We left its cool interior for the hot and heavy air outside and began to walk toward the great stone ruin.

The neighborhood of a shrine such as this becomes a sort of perpetual carnival area. Rows of little stalls house the shops where a thousand kinds of things are sold. We stopped to watch a vendor frying *chipatis,* a sort of Pakistani pancake. In one part of the large pan were the chipatis, in another the coins he was getting in payment!

We reached the shrine and ascended a long flight of stone stairs. We entered a large chamber. The air was heavy with the scent of flowers. In the center was the tomb of the original saint of this shrine. The sarcophagus was almost covered with sweet-smelling flowers. Many coins, little offerings of the many visitors, sparkled among the petals. We stood for awhile watching the people come and go.

A wicked-looking fellow with a huge black moustache had

attached himself to our little party. He now indicated another
flight of stairs and we followed him down them. We descended
a very considerable distance. We soon realized from the damp-
ness and relative coolness that we were beneath the surface of
the earth. We came out from the stairway into a large cave with
earthern walls dimly lit with oil lamps. Proceeding from a dark
and narrow extension at one end of it was a stream of clear
water. Every now and then, a man carrying a bucket would
emerge from the darkness and bear the precious fluid away.
Here, as in many of these shrines, a spring of sweet water had
been one of the original attractions.

Our self-appointed guide now indicated a narrow flight of
stairs, and we followed him upward, a long climb. As we reached
the top, we felt a breath of air—warm, but with a bit of the
freshness of the sea in it. We were on a broad terrace, under a
peaceful, moonlit sky; there in the distance were the sparkling
waters of the Arabian Sea. Directly in front of us was the figure
of a man—a very large man seated on the stone, in a relaxed
posture. This was the holy man—the present-day saint of the
shrine. Even though he was seated, and we standing, the impression of height and robustness which he gave was remarkable.
He was dressed in white and wore a large white moustache.
His skin was relatively pale. Our guide spoke a few words to
him, and he nodded gravely. Then the guide turned to us, "He
speaks only Pushtu," he said, "the language of Afghanistan,
whence he came several years ago." Then he added, as an extra,
"He is 70 years of age—and he spent thirty-six years of his life
immersed in hot oil"(!)

Through translation, we carried on some communication with
the holy man. He made a somewhat prophetic utterance or
two about the younger members of our group. Apparently we
all seemed reverent enough, for the interview was a pleasant
one. We received his blessing when we left, and I do not believe
that it ever has done us any harm, although my concept of his
religious affiliations and attitudes was a rather dim one.

* * *

Modern Pakistan is certainly a land of great and amazing

contrasts. For many million, the holiness of the saint whom we visited is one of the most real and important things in the world—nor are his years of immersion in hot oil to be denied by them; yet, in many instances the culture and learning of the ancient East and the modern West have been joined in brilliant minds like that of my colleague, Mohammed Ishaq. No one is more aware of the contrasts in his own country, nor of the long path ahead, than the educated Pakistani. Speaking of the visitor's view of the land, Ishaq said to me in correspondence after my own return to the States; "Little does he realize that what he sees is a hundred times improved, as compared to what things were in 1947—and this despite the many political ordeals and tortures the country has been, and is, passing through. Yet, it is a long way before we catch up with the rest of the world in the various fields of education, literature and science."

Ishaq's own views on the relationship of basic to applied science, on the responsibility of the scientist to humanity and on the relationship between peoples and nations would form a treatise of the most progressive and enlightened type. He seems to be himself one of those to whom reference is made in the Holy Koran (II, 269): "And he unto whom WISDOM is given, he truly hath received abundant good." He is far removed from the picture of the cold and unfeeling scientist. His is the type of mind which aspires for his people and for humanity as they stumble toward the light . . .

> Then to the rolling Heav'n itself I cried,
> Asking, "What Lamp had Destiny to guide
> Her little Children stumbling in the Dark?"
> And—"A blind Understanding!" Heav'n replied.

> . . . .

> Ah, Love! could thou and I with Fate conspire
> To grasp this sorry Scheme of Things entire,
> Would not we shatter it to bits—and then
> Remould it nearer to the Heart's Desire!

Chapter 17

JOURNEY TO JAMNAGAR

A Visit to Doctor H. C. Srivastava in Gujarat, India

I HAD TAKEN out my small camera. As the plane descended through a mass of gray clouds, I held it ready for a first view of the coast of India. The gracious stewardess of Pakistan International Airlines saw my intention. She stepped over quickly, and just as I realized that she was going to admonish me against picture-taking, the plane took a sudden drop, and neither of us could say a word for a moment. We both laughed, and I put the camera away.

The airport was far out, some sixteen miles from the center of Bombay. As I left the plane, I felt the heavy, warm and humid atmosphere of the place, one which was not changed as I entered the airport building, for air-conditioning at this port was confined to the restaurant. The Bombay airport is a busy one. Crowds of people in most varied costumes were coming and going. I was met, through previous arrangement, by a travel representative.

Mr. Advani was a personable young man. When he greeted me, in friendly fashion, with a "Happy Birthday, sir," I really was taken aback for a moment! Then I realized that, being familiar with my papers, he would know that this day of arrival in Bombay really was my birthday.

I was on my way to the city of Jamnagar to visit Doctor Harish Chandra Srivastava, an Indian anatomist with whom I had become acquainted two years before in the States. He had been carrying out research work at the University of Michigan and had represented that school at a meeting at my own department in Indiana, when the Midwest Society of Anatomists had met

224

FIGURE 33 Harish Chandra Srivastava.

there. In the conferences and on social occasions, I had been much impressed by this "Midwest man from the East."

After the usual formalities of customs, we loaded my bags into the car and started for the city. The road was a good one, but we had not gone far when we began passing clusters of huts of astonishing squalor. They were the most makeshift structures that I had ever seen, far outdoing even those in the refugee camps at Karachi.

"Are people living here?" I ask Advani. The area seemed peculiarly lifeless. He made a deprecatory gesture. "These," he said, "are temporary homes of men and their wives who work

on different job-projects near the harbor." So this was an Indian
version of our "two pay check" way of life in the United States.

We soon were in the streets of Bombay. We passed some
beautiful buildings—an ornate Hindu temple, then a Buddhist
temple with graceful, tapering spires. Here there were no
camels on the streets, nor any of the motor bike "rickshas" of
Karachi. There was a good deal of auto traffic. There also were
lumbering two-wheel ox-carts. In the outlying streets, beautiful
Indian cows were not uncommon and seemed wholly unper-
turbed by the traffic.

Bombay is the largest commercial city in India, second only
in size to Calcutta. The mills and their smoke, however, are kept
to the outskirts. The city proper has a lovely natural setting. We
now drove along a magnificent boulevard, curving with the
sweep of the bay. Imposing buildings lined the boulevard on
one side, while on the other a wide walk ran along above the
beach.

I planned to stay in Bombay for several days, then to fly
north to the Province of Gujarat on the Gulf of Cutch. I had
chosen the Taj Mahal Hotel as my headquarters. The hotel is
one of the buildings along the great seafront boulevard. Just
at this place, however, is a large open space known as Apollo
Bunder, which reaches out into the harbor. Dominating the
whole area is the exotic and imposing structure known as the
Gateway to India. It was hard for me to know whether I was
impressed more by the gateway or by the hotel itself.

The Gateway of India was built to commemorate the visit of
King George V and Queen Mary in 1911. It is a massive yet
graceful structure, built in the sixteenth century Gujarat style
of architecture.

The central portion was a high rectangle with a slender
tower, surmounted by a spire, built into each of the four angles.
The gateway itself was a high pointed arch. On either side,
great wings extended from the central structure. The whole area
about the gateway and under the arches was a colorful scene
with hundreds of persons in varied costumes enjoying the
breezes from the bay. I later learned that the spaces within the
gateway itself can accommodate 600 people! On the opposite

side of the open area was the Taj Mahal Hotel. It is a block-long building put up under British supervision, but very much in Indian, or *Mogul* style, dating from the turn of the century. A high central dome gives it an imposing aspect.

We pulled up at the door of the hotel, and my bags were whisked away. At the desk I registered and changed ten British pounds for 135 Indian rupees. As my bags were being carried to the elevator, I was impressed suddenly by a very pleasant and cool sensation. There was a delightful breeze here. The reason was soon apparent. A completely open shaft or air way occupied the central part of the building, rising up eight stories to the great dome. The stairways bordered this shaft, and many rooms opened from the wide landings on each floor. The elevator stopped at one of these landings. My room was a long, rather narrow one. At one end, however, there were three windows which opened out directly upon the harbor, with a view of the great open space, the Apollo Bunder and the Gateway to India.

I took a shower and made a few telephone calls. My chief initial contact in Bombay was to be with Doctor Ramchandani, a young professor at the King Edward Memorial Hospital and Medical School. We arranged to meet the next morning.

After a brief rest, I dressed for dinner and went down to the mezzanine where the large, air-conditioned dining room was located. I had a very fine lamb cutlet, some unidentified pudding and coffee. A little later, at the Xanadu bar on the same floor I ran into my guide of the day, Mr. Advani, whose business took him often to the Taj Mahal.

Since it was still fairly early when I left him, I decided on a short stroll outside. The Apollo Bunder was well lighted, and I walked across to the Gateway to India, enjoying the variety and motion all about me. On the return walk, I happened to pass along another side of the hotel, one to which the bright lights did not penetrate. Under the arches were scores and scores of shapeless dark heaps, passing the night as best they could. These, too, were the people of India.

* * *

Doctor Ramchandani and I were driving up Comballa Hill in the bright morning sun. He was a very good companion and already had told me a great deal about Bombay and its medical schools—there were three of them at that time.

"I am taking you first to the King Edward Memorial Hospital," he said. "The school of medicine connected with it has a rather long name—The Seth Gorhandas Sunderdas Medical College." A short way farther on, we turned in to the entrance of a large stone building. He led the way up the stairs and into the office of the professor of anatomy. A young assistant greeted us. Evidently I had been expected. "The professor should be here shortly," he said. "Would you like to see the dissecting laboratory?"

"Very much," I replied. After all, this was my very first human anatomy laboratory in India, and I was very curious and eager. I took off my jacket and donned a white coat which was offered to me.

The laboratory was just down the hall. I am not sure just what I had expected, but I found a large, airy room with a not unpleasant atmosphere, tables well-spaced and an air of order and cleanliness. Doctor Ramchandani and the assistant had accompanied me, and as we entered, the students looked at us respectfully—and at me somewhat curiously. "It is a quiet part of our day," the assistant said. "We have to have each body divided among sixteen students. The dissection of any one body must be limited to three months—our climate, you know." I walked around the laboratory and examined a few dissections in some detail: a thyroid gland with its blood and nerve supply exposed; a brachial plexus, that great complex of nerves for the shoulder and arm, with a beautiful demonstration of its medial and lateral cords and of the large nerves arising from it, the median, musculocutaneous and radial, and the muscles of the lateral aspect of the neck.

I now saw some bodies that puzzled me; I did not know whether they were the real thing or models! In answer to my inquiry, the assistant took me over to them, and the answer was clear—they were *mummified* bodies! "Yes, we use these a good deal," he told me. "They are very good for surface anatomy and for marking out the underlying organs. And they last very well!"

Being a professor, I hardly could resist quizzing some of these students. They responded very well indeed.

One very real difference between this Indian laboratory and our American ones was the proportion of women students. They made up about 50 per cent of the class. Many of them were beautiful, all of them were feminine and their white coats did not conceal the fact that they were wearing the traditional saris.

We went into the museum, a large room adjoining. Here were plastic models of various parts of the body, many of them made by the students. Comparative anatomy and embryology were not neglected among the specimens.

Now we proceeded down the hall to the histology laboratory, a room with long tables for microscopic work. It was interesting to me to learn that histology here had become a part of anatomy, as it is in the medical schools of the United States. For many years in Great Britain and in English possessions, the histology (microscopic anatomy) had been a subject in the department of physiology, and I knew that the changeover was occurring in a number of universities in England. There were fairly good arguments either way. One could not talk very much about microscopic structure of the organs without discussing *function*, the chief topic of physiology, but, then, histology *is* microscopic anatomy. In any event, bridges had to be built between the old disciplines, and anatomy itself was becoming more functional all the time.

Meanwhile the professor of anatomy, Doctor K. D. Desai, had joined us. He was most cordial, although he seemed a little surprised that we already had been visiting the gross laboratory. I asked him a few questions about the medical curriculum and learned that anatomy and physiology both continue through the first two years (in our American schools they usually are completed in the first year). "The total medical school course," Desai told me, "is four and one-half years. Then come six months of a rural or 'social' internship."

Ramchandani and I took our leave of the anatomy department and went down the hall to medicine. Here in a large and fully carpeted office we met the professor of medicine, Doctor Raghaven. His special interest was in the field of involuntary movements, and he had spent some of his training time in Chicago. The hospital and medical school were all in the one large building, and we now visited a number of the clinical laboratories. At the radioisotope laboratory I was told that the Atomic Energy Commission of India, like our own Atomic Energy Commission, makes large quantities of isotopes, such as Iodine 131, available to laboratories throughout the country. Thus far they have been used chiefly in a clinical way, rather than for fundamental research.

As we walked down a long corridor which was open on one side, I could not help remarking on the excellent design, which kept a really fresh, cool air in this huge structure in its tropical setting. Ramchandani agreed on its efficacy. "Actually," he said, "King Edward Memorial was built, like most of our more recent hospitals, on the pavillion system of the Germans. It was begun in 1925 and now has 750 beds."

We had a quick visit to a surgical amphitheater, not going far enough in to make it necessary for us to scrub. We then paid a visit to the office of the dean, simply for an introduction, for he, like deans in our country, was in the middle of several duties at once.

A stop at the department of pathology was of considerable interest. Here I learned that the *class*, not each student, receives a set of slides and that group study is made by projection of the slides. The professor of pathology, Doctor N. M. Purandare, took us to the pathology museum. Just outside the door was a bust of the benefactor who, by his gifts, had made the founding and upkeep of the museum possible. It was a large museum with a comprehensive collection of well-mounted pathological specimens.

We went on to pharmacology and talked with Professor V. K. Sheth, head of the department. Things were torn up there, but for a good cause—a general expansion of the department. "We are interested particularly in psychopharmacology," Sheth said, "and our laboratories are being reoriented toward that kind of work." He showed me a number of mice in a drug-induced sleep. "Some of them," he said, pointing to one whose whiskers were twitching, "are dreamers!"

By this time I was about ready to sit down for awhile and was glad to have Ramchandani tell me that tea was being served at mid-morning back in the anatomy department. We drank very strong tea and ate cookies in Professor Desai's office. I learned a little more about the course work and the texts. As a matter of fact, the chief text required turned out to be the same as ours—Cunningham's *Textbook of Anatomy*. Before we left, an arrangement had been made for me to present a lecture on the following day at the medical school.

* * *

The streets were teeming with life and activity as we drove over to visit the second medical school of Bombay—Topiwala. The atmosphere there was considerably different. The architecture of the building and the plan of laboratories and lecture rooms were far more modern. It seemed, too, as though the research and the attitudes of the faculty went along with the theme of modernity. The professor of histology, for example, Doctor Eustace J. De Souza, was an enthusiast for studies in histochemistry and was actively engaged in this field of investigation. He showed me some fine, up-to-date equipment of which he had every reason to be proud. The incubator and ovens were of Swiss manufacture. The photomicrography was of high quality. De Souza projected slides in his office, showing us the results of studies on the enzyme succinic dehydrogenase in a variety of tissues and cells, including white blood cells, muscle and sperm. He had followed the changes in amount of this enzyme also in various physiological and pathological conditions.

After the projection, we stepped into the larger common room of the department. From the window there was a beautiful view. De Souza pointed to the distant heights. "That," he said, "is Malabar Hill, and the shining dome belongs to the famous Maharaja of Gwalior." Gwalior is one of the states of Central India very well known for its excellent ceramic work.

On the drive back to the hotel, Ramchandani and I talked on more general and less scientific topics. He told me how important for the historical record in India were the Asoka Pillars.

Asoka-vardhana was a great ruler who came to power about 270 B.C. He fought a fierce war with a neighboring kingdom. Although victorious, he was appalled to see the suffering which the war brought. From this conquest, he turned away and toward the path of Buddhism, the chief conquest, the conquest by the law of piety or duty (*dharma*). In order to spread the knowledge of Buddhist *dharma*, he had a series of inscriptions made on pillars and great stones throughout his dominions, which eventually included almost all of India. These inscriptions contained much of historical importance. Asoka, too, sent missionaries to other countries of Asia and spread the teachings of the Buddha far and wide, making of Buddhism one of the chief religions of the world.

How did we come to be talking of Asoka? I had asked about the engraving on a piece of currency—a beautiful picture of the capital of an Asoka pillar, on which were seated three lions. "Buddhism left India almost entirely, to flourish in other countries," Ramchandani said, "but Asoka remains a great hero, like your George Washington."

"Do you like your accommodations?" my friend asked me. "I surely do," I replied, "It is a wonderful old hotel."

"The name," Ramchandani said, "simply means Royal Palace." I thought for a moment of the faery building far to the north, at Agra, where Italian architectural genius had combined with the wonders of the Arabian Nights to create a building that was one great jewel—the Taj Mahal! There was little real resemblance—but it *was* a good hotel.

Before he left me at the hotel, Ramchandani had arranged to come next morning to take me to the lecture hall and for some additional visits. I was free for the afternoon—free in Bombay!

I enjoyed a good lunch—consommé, hot-pot of lamb and tea. I skipped the ice cream but ate two small pastries. The dining room was an interesting panorama for me, with turbaned Hindus and Sikhs, flat-capped Parsees and a few westerners. The weather was warm but pleasant, and I went out for a stroll. Only a few blocks from the hotel I came upon a huge building, the Prince of Wales Museum. The probable coolness of the interior was almost as much a lure as the exhibitions, and I went in. The first hall contained case after case of weapons, from all parts of India and all historical periods. The next held a display of books—or *sutras*—with marvellously colored illustrations. The beautiful Sanskrit lettering had been done by hand. What a tremendous amount of work and devotion was represented by such books from old India! I scarcely could help thinking of the modern flood of paperbacks.

I wandered into another hall, where there were many examples of ancient Indian sculpture. Two westerners were being guided about here by a tall Sikh with full black beard and stately turban. The fact that I was alone gave me a little feeling of being more of a native, and this was increased by the bilingual arrangement of the labels on the museum objects. A description in English followed that in Hindi. I was able, with a knowledge of the Devangari alphabet and a very little self-taught Hindi, to make out the words and syllables. I paused before a figure of Vishnu, the Preserver, stretched out upon the great snake, Sesha. In his role of redeeming and preserving, Vishnu has had to appear in many forms, often as an animal, once in very ancient times as Krishna, and also as the great hero Rama. There were statues here, too, of the "vehicle of Vishnu," the strange and awful bird known as the Garuda—strange and awful in its sculpture form, but actually representing the kite or Malabar eagle, a bird which perhaps gained some of the reverence owed to it by its excellent work as a snake killer.

Leaving this area, I came to a wide stairway. Looking upward, I beheld the interior of the dome of the museum, a magnificent piece of architecture, reminding me of the dome of our United States National Museum in Washington.

On the second floor I looked at collections of china, pottery and cut glass from England. While I was standing near a beautiful statue of a lion and lioness, a large group of children were led through the room in a quiet and orderly procession. As each one stared curiously at me, I felt very much like a part of the collections.

In a gallery of paintings I was surprised to see an excellent oil of Abraham Lincoln. It had been purchased by a Parsee merchant of Bombay who was travelling in America at the time of the assassination of Lincoln.

I ended my museum trip with a visit to the natural history division. There was a great deal of interesting material, but I was impressed most by the magnificent Stag of Kashmir and the Great Indian Hornbill, the male of which shuts up his mate in a hollow tree and feeds her through the nesting period.

When I came out of the museum, a light rain was falling. I stayed on the museum porch for awhile and fell into conversation with a gentleman who, like me, was carrying a *Guide to Bombay*. He was from Hyderabad and complained about the difficulty of understanding the Hindi. In his own city, he told me, they speak Telegu, but with an *Urdu* accent, which in turn exasperates the country people who come to town with their "pure" Telegu! His name was B. Vasudevarao, B.A., B.L. Perhaps I may meet him again one day.

By the time I returned to the hotel, it was the hour for dinner. Afterwards, I reviewed a few notes for the morning lecture, watched the heaving waters of the bay from my window, and turned in.

Before my lecture at the Seth Gorhandas Sunderdas Medical College (G.S.M.C.), Doctor Ramchandani took me to visit the Grant Medical College (G.M.C.). This was in a building over fifty years old but well built and with large, high-ceilinged laboratories. The dissection room was equipped with marble-topped tables, a good contribution toward cooling the atmosphere in general. A high proportion of young ladies were at work, some at all-women tables, others with men, much as in our own classes.

Here I had an opportunity for a close inspection of a mummified body. It had been dried thoroughly and then shellacked, thus giving an almost indestructible specimen.

The professor of gross anatomy, Doctor V. B. Pathak, told

me that the identity of the cadavers and source are carefully kept, and the information is available to the students. Professor Pathak had worked at Bristol, England, with Professor Yoffey, whom we had visited there some years earlier and whose work on lymphocytes was world-renowned. We visited the post-graduate laboratory for research in histology, where I talked with a woman faculty member. In the adjoining laboratory of embryology, there were attractive displays of developmental stages of the chick. Here also was a huge brain microtome, of a type seldom seen.

We passed on into the Laboratory of general human histology. Here I was greeted by Doctor N. B. D. K. D. Desai. Recalling Doctor Pathak's stay with Professor Yoffey, I asked, "Have you had an opportunity to work outside of India?" "Well, yes," he said. "As a matter of fact, while Pathak was in England, I was in your country, doing research at the University of Colorado, with Doctor Buchanan." Here was another familiar name, for Buchanan had recently used two photomicrographs from my research in his book *Functional Neuroanatomy.*

We left the school building and walked over to the great hospital. I remarked on the size of the building. "There are some 1,200 beds in all in this compound," Ramchandani told me. "Much of it is charity. If a person's income is less than 150 rupees per month, he pays nothing here." In the spacious entry hall there was a great statue of the Parsee benefactor of the hospital. There was also a place for contributions, and I dropped a small coin in the slot—somewhat like dropping a pebble in the ocean.

My friend now took me in to see the dean, Doctor Virkar, who asked me to convey best wishes to our dean in Indiana. We returned to the office of Professor Pathak. While we waited for Doctor Desai, he told me about his former position "five years in an out-of-the-way school." He had been here at G.M.C. only three weeks. "Of course, I might be transferred again," he said. This was a type of uncertainty which faculty members in the United States do not have, I thought, although voluntary moves are common enough.

Doctor Desai arrived, and we drove over to the G.S.M.C. I was introduced to the professor of surgery, who asked me to sign his visitors' book. As I took the pen, I noticed a name just a few lines above the current one. It was that of Charles M. Pomerat, the well-known cytologist, whose excellent motion pictures of tissue cultures have been so widely known and admired.

The office of the professor of surgery was a little more elegant than those of the basic science men. It was a good place to relax before a lecture in a strange city. I mentioned to him that I had been impressed by the number of Indian scientists who had studied and worked abroad. "Yes, there are many opportunities," he said, with a somewhat quizzical smile. "Of course, it doesn't always turn out as well as it might." He then told me of a man who had spent nine years in England. On his return to India, he seemed unable to find satisfaction in any of the opportunities open to him. As I write this, I am reminded of a Peruvian who spent some time in our department at Indiana. His letters, after his return, amazed us by the trail of bad luck and even outright resentment that seemed to attend him after his foreign experience.

Doctor Desai and I now went down to the anteroom of the large lecture hall. The Indian style of welcome to a lecturer was something for which I was totally unprepared. As we entered the hall, a tremendous tumult broke out—clapping, foot-stamping and various assorted kinds of noise-making. After what seemed several minutes of this, a quiet fell, and I was introduced by Desai. I spoke for about an hour, largely on recent studies with the electron microscope and their relation to problems of age changes in tissues. I seldom have had so attentive an audience. After a few questions from the floor, we retired to the anteroom, and tea was served to a group of the faculty members. When Ramchandani called for me, I left the G.S.M.C. with many expressions of mutual good will.

My host had asked me if there were any places in or around Bombay which I would like to see. Actually, I had looked forward with much interest to seeing the Elephant Caves, with their ancient sculptures of Hindu divinities, but these were located on a nearby island, and the violence of the sea in this monsoon season made the voyage so dangerous that small ships had ceased to go there. But there were other fascinating possibilities. "I would like very much to see one of the Towers of Silence," I said. These are the places where the Parsees dispose of their dead, towers placed high on hilltops where the bodies can be sighted readily by the agents of disposal—the ever-present vultures, or kites, that wheel in the Indian skies.

We drove up a steep hill to an establishment of this type. Non-Parsees could not enter nor ascend the tower itself but we talked with one of the officials there, a Mr. Patel, who had just completed the "burial" of his father-in-law at this tower. The body of the deceased is carefully prepared for this final scene. The Parsee feels that he has done the very finest thing possible for his loved ones in this type of disposal, strange and even gruesome as it may seem to us.

After viewing the tower itself from a distance of some hundred yards, and the vultures, which after all are a common enough sight, we drove on toward the center of the city. We detoured, however, to go up on Malabar Hill, with its hanging gardens, a beautiful parklike area. Here a boy with a trained monkey persuaded us to pose for pictures—with his companion!

Ramchandani did me a final favor by helping me to select a beautiful sari at a shop in downtown Bombay. Then, at the Taj Mahal, I said goodbye to this friend of so few hours but so many experiences.

As it already was past midafternoon, I had a light lunch of cold roast beef and tea. I had planned a little individual trip in the city and had spotted an interesting looking bookstore— the Tareporevala. I would taxi there, a little over a mile, then walk back through the teeming streets. I spent an hour or so in the store and emerged with two small books, the *Songs of Bullah* and *Introducing Zoroastriananism with 52 Weekly Sermons*. Bullah was a Sufi saint, one of those who have had some softening influence in the frequently bitter religious conflicts of the subcontinent. Zoroastrianism is, of course, the ancient Persian religion of which the Parsees are heirs.

The walk back was on busy thoroughfares, with many fine stores and also smaller shops with a tremendous variety of wares. In this part of Bombay, almost all of the people were well clothed and evidently about as prosperous as the people in the downtown of my own city, Indianapolis. I saw my first pith helmet of the trip, topping a westerner. I was approached once or twice by beggars, but in a civil enough way and as though not too much depended on the outcome. At one small stationery shop I bought some beautiful stamps from the Mongolian People's Republic. The people and animals depicted were Mongolian, but the writing was Russian. I came to the campus of the University of Bombay and passed close to its great tower. A cup of tea at Green's Hotel, across the street from my own, completed my little journey.

That evening I had an early dinner and was ready for bed by 10:30. After all, the morning call was for 4:15 A.M., and Jamnagar was waiting.

* * *

Early as it was, the room service brought me coffee, an orange and cookies before 4:30 A.M. When I had finished this light but welcome repast, I called for the porter. He appeared, in a bright orange turban, promptly placed my two suitcases on top of it and left for the lobby. I followed and soon was on the airport bus. I found myself seated by a young American. His name was Charles Leslie, and he was en route to Hyderabad. He spoke of the Nizam, reputed at one time to be the world's wealthiest man, and of his fabulous art collection. Leslie had been at Jamnagar; in fact, he had been the guest of the Maharajah there on one occasion and now was somewhat concerned as to just how to address him in a thank you note!

The airport building was a busy and variegated scene, and I had a little more time to look around than upon my arrival in Bombay. Leslie and I continued talking until his plane to Hyderabad was called. As I waited for my own flight, I again was impressed by the many costumes and racial types seen in an Indian crowd. Near me a tall Sikh, with heavy beard and handsome turban, was standing. He looked every inch a fighting man, but instead of a weapon he was carrying a book.

My flight, IAC 129, was called. The plane was an eighteen-passenger Viscount. Our take-off was excellent, and the flight generally steady and pleasant, although, flying at a fairly low altitude, we did hit a few rough places in the clouds. In the seat across from me was a Parsee gentleman who was reading and speaking to himself, perhaps repeating prayers or religious verses. I thought of how familiar to me the Parsees seemed now, when a few weeks before *Thus Spake Zarathustra* was about all that would come to mind if one mentioned the ancient religion of Zoroaster. Actually, there was a close relationship between these people and the Gujarat, to which I was flying. When the Arabs conquered Persia in the eighth century, large groups of Persians had emigrated. They landed first at Din in Kathiawar, but less than twenty years later moved to Sanjan on the Gujarat coast and right up to the present the vernacular language of the Parsees is Gujarati. It was not until 1640 that they began their settlements in Bombay. Their wanderings remind one of our pilgrim fathers from England to the Netherlands and to the "wild New England Shore," but the durability of their character is far more like that of the Jewish people. This latter similarity extends also to their almost uncanny skill in business and finance. The man in the seat in front of the Parsee was engrossed in a newspaper in Gujarati, of which I knew just about enough to distinguish it from the Hindi. Except for me, there were no Americans nor Europeans on this flight.

There were occasional glimpses of the ground between the clouds but few details.

At 9:10 A.M. we descended at Rajkat for a fifteen-minute stop. Here we are, I was thinking, really in the "Indians' India." As I entered the little airport building, I was slightly taken aback to see a sign, "Lions' Club of Rajkat Welcomes Visiting Lions"! It was cooler outside, so I walked out to mingle with the people who had come apparently to see the plane land or to wait for a flight. Here, though, the costumes and appear-

ances really were far more "Indian" than in Bombay. A group
of women came by, all of them dressed in beautiful dark red
garments. One man resembled in costume and in bearing a
Zouave of the French army. Another huge fellow in turban was
a real story-book figure.

Back on the plane, I saw the red-roofed houses of Rajkat and
the small river nearby as we took off. In what seemed a short
time we were descending again, and this time, when the wheels
hit ground, I knew that we were at Jamnagar! Yet I was very
much surprised as we alighted. There, in front of us, was a
large military plane. Its bright orange markings reminded me
of our own planes which come and go so frequently in Bermuda
where we had been working in marine biology.

I had a brief moment or two of disappointment in finding
no one to greet me at the port. I had to decide quickly, however, whether to go into town or to wait, as the bus was about
to leave. Thinking that my friend might be waiting to meet me
in the town, I took the bus. It was an interesting, if somewhat
lonesome, ride. We drove along a good but unpaved road. We
passed two Sikhs on bicycles with brilliant red and pink turbans,
several camels, and a whole herd of water buffalo. As we entered
the city of Jamnagar, I noted another sign in English, "The
Lions' Club of Jamnagar Heartily Welcomes You"!

On the bus, an official of the airline had very thoughtfully
asked me if I were being met. Obviously I seemed a little off
the beaten track for my kind, and he surely had my best interests at heart. I told him that I thought so. As we pulled into
the yard of the airlines office, I saw with great pleasure and
just a little relief, my good friend Doctor H. C. Srivastava, waiting with a broad smile of welcome!

"Welcome to Jamnagar!" Srivastava exclaimed, grasping my
hand. It did indeed seem as though I had reached the goal of a
pilgrimage. I was in Jamnagar. The *Bhagavadgita* in my suit-
case, a volume which Srivastava, in Michigan, had obtained
from India, and sent to me in Indiana, had come full circle.

We drove over the short distance to the government guest
house, where I was to stay. It was a British structure, apparently

with postindependence Indian additions—a large, white building set in spacious grounds, well fenced in. A painted carving
greeted us at the entrance. It was Ganesha, elephant god of the
Hindus, seated like a prosperous merchant. He has a really
appealing combination of animal and human characteristics. Incidentally, his story contains an account of a more-than-ordinary
type of organ-grafting. The son of Siva and Durga, a sad accident
occurred to him as a baby. A fond but apparently warm gaze
from his mother, Durga, reduced his human head to ashes. Siva
gave instructions that the head of the first creature encountered
who would be sleeping with its face toward the north should
be used to replace the lost one. Well, of course, the animal encountered was an elephant—and the graft took very successfully!

The weather was very hot. Under the heat the compound
seemed unusually still after the noise of the streets. Every now
and then a weird cry came through the air, one which I had
been told in Pakistan is that of the brain-fever bird. I asked my
friend about it. "Oh, that," he said. "We call it the cuckoo bird."
This seemed appropriate enough to me, even if the cry were
unlike anything in our own country.

Inside the guest house, it was much cooler, and there was
even a light breeze blowing through my apartment, situated at
the front of the main floor, one flight above the ground. Doctor
Srivastava arranged to pick me up later in the afternoon. "The
Jains have dinner rather early," he told me. The type of Hinduism which predominates in the Gujarat is that of the Jains. This
sect has a long and complex history. Its members claim to be
the real descendents of the ancient Brahmin penitents, whose
doctrines and usages they have tried to protect from the "sac-
rilegious" innovations of the modern Brahmins and of the Budd-
hists alike. Actually, I must confess that during this visit to India
I was really concerned on more than one occasion that I might
offend someone in relation to matters of religion—far more so
than in relation to politics or international affairs.

After a shower, I went in to lunch. There were only a few
persons lodging at the guest house. One was a Mr. Jarat of the
Electrical Commission, another was a lady, wife of an income

tax official. Mr. Jarat told me some interesting facts about the large export of salt, obtained from sea water, from this region. He talked also about the ten-year old prohibition of alcoholic liquor and the benefits which the action had brought to India. Apparently there was some language difficulty between Mr. Jarat and the waiters, for he expressed surprise at the order in which the courses were served—the chipatis and a huge flaky object, name unknown to me, were brought out first.

We left the dining room. In the lobby there were several Parsees sitting about and talking. With the large picture of Patel, a noted leader of their religion and an Indian statesman of note, conspicuous on the wall, it seemed very much a Parsee gathering. After awhile I returned to my own quarters, which were on the same floor. They certainly were spacious enough: the bedroom with two beds, each hung with somber black mosquito netting; a living room with two tables, six chairs and a couch, and a huge bathroom. I got inside the mosquito netting and napped pleasantly for nearly two hours. It was getting into the late afternoon when I awoke, and by the time that I had showered and dressed, Doctor Srivastava arrived, accompanied by a young medical student. By this time also a very welcome breeze had sprung up outside.

The three of us sat down to tea in the lobby. "The place to which we wish to take you this afternoon," my friend said, "is called in Hindi, the *Shamshanghat*. In Gujarati, it is *Sonapuri*. We are going in my student's automobile." I knew vaguely what a *ghat* would be—a place where the bodies of Hindu believers are cremated. But I did not know what happened after the cremation, nor why grounds of any extent would be needed at such a place.

We drove for some distance and left the busy streets behind. We passed through a gateway. Suddenly we were in still another world. This world was peopled by some of the most striking and beautiful figures which I have ever seen, statues of life size or more. It was not only their forms which were impressive, but also the vivid colors in which they were painted—colors which truly seemed to give them the warm breath of life.

I have thought at the time, and since, how we often forget
that the marvellous statues of ancient days also were painted in
bright hues. Our reproductions of such statues in the public
places of the modern world almost invariably are only the natural white or gray of the stone, representing the ancient figures
as they have come down to us, but the writings of those times,
such as those of Pausanias, often describe in vivid terms the
painted figures as they then existed. In a way, then, I not only
had traveled ten thousand miles in space but over two thousand
years backward in time!

The statues were ranged along a broad pathway. First was
a bearded saintlike figure, standing erect. A few paces on was
a figure in the seated position, like the familiar Buddha, but of
course, in this location, only *Hindu* saints were to be found.
Further on, I could not help stopping in front of another figure,
for it had an appearance of true divinity. "That is Krishna,"
Doctor Srivastava told me, "and you will note the man beside
him in the chariot—it is Arjuna." Of course, these were the
characters of the *Bhagavadgita*, the divine Krishna, the in-
carnate God of the Hindus, in his last avatar or earthly form as
the chariot driver, and the valiant Arjuna, the leader of the
Pandava forces in a titanic struggle against the Kauravas. The
chariot and trappings here were rich with gold. A little way
further on stood Mahatma Gandhi, secure in his sainthood.

We now approached a place where the path turned at right
angles. Here was the site of cremation. This was a paved area,
about twenty by forty feet, without ornamentation. Near it was
a representation of a great wheel with symbolic figures along its
periphery. "This," said my friend, "is Chakra, the Wheel of Life."

I saw now that the figures represented the stages in life's
journey, beginning with the cutting of the umbilical cord, passing
through infancy, adolescence, marriage and maturity on to old
age and death. It gave one, at this scene of the final rites, not so
much a feeling of sadness as of the universality of the elements
in the history of each human being, and made me think, as with
Bryant: "All that breathe will share thy destiny. . ."

Beyond the crematorium, we came on a statue of Hanuman,

the heroic monkey god of the splendid Hindu epic known as the *Ramayana*. In his robust chest was shown his heart, and within it stood the figures of Prince Rama and his princess, Sita. Hanuman is the Hindu ideal of the loyal henchman, an individual whose whole glory is in service to his beloved master. He was commander-in-chief of the army of the monkeys which aided Rama in the attack on Lankah (Ceylon) to rescue Sita from the grasp of the wicked giant Ravana.

More figures, each one a strikingly individualistic presentation of a god or saint, lined the path as we proceeded. Here was a man who had helped to revive Hinduism and to drive out Buddhism, after the latter religion had spread widely in India. He had been canonized for his deeds. There was a blind bard, carrying a musical instrument, an Indian Homer, perhaps! Here was Sita, wife of Rama, with two charming babies in a little hut in the forest. There was Krishna, as a shepherd with a flute. As an incarnation of the Supreme Being, born to avenge the misdeeds of a tyrant, he had been exchanged with the daughter of a shepherd to save him from the tyrant's wrath— hence he was brought up in a pastoral life. Next we came upon the figure of a great Rajput warrior who had fought against the Moguls, who were invading the country. Then there were two boy saints, each of whom had combatted his wicked father.

Here was a figure telling a dramatic story, a young mother carrying a dead child to a site of cremation where a noble-appearing man awaited. Doctor Srivastava told me the story:

A king and his family had lost their throne and fortune. The king had become keeper of a crematorium. Their young son had died, and here was the mother bringing him to be cremated. But the king, ever honest and upright, even amid the direst circumstances, had to require that his wife pay the appropriate fee. To do this she tore her raiment and turned over a part of it. Then Heaven, or the gods, seeing how much they had suffered and how good they were, finally smiled upon them, apparently bringing the boy back to life and the family to prosperity.

A little farther on was the figure of a young man carrying

his two blind parents on his back. "He was taking them," my friend told me, "on a pilgrimage to a holy place." In one part of the Shamshanghat was a large relief map of India, spread out on the ground, with a low wall about it. The Himalayas were represented realistically by great stones.

"There are four chief holy places for the Hindus," Doctor Srivastava told me. "One is near here, another is in the East, at Orissa, a third in the North, at Benares, and a fourth is in the South." The relief map was beautifully done. There were Ceylon and the smaller islands, the Nicobars and Andamans. There were the valleys of the great rivers, the Ganges, the Indus and the others.

We now had completed the circuit, and we left by the gate at which we had entered. Near this gate was a fine statue of India's great poet, Rabindranath Tagore. I recalled a recent session of our Poets' Corner group in Indianapolis, where one of our members had described his recollections from long ago. Tagore, a Nobel prize winner in literature, had made a visit to the University of Illinois while our speaker had been a student there. The profound impression which his great personality had made remained with him through the years.

Back in the car, we drove directly to the busy streets of Jamnagar. The streets were busy indeed, and crowded not only with human beings but also with cows, goats, dogs, donkeys and an occasional camel. At one place a tremendous heavily horned ox stood immobile exactly in the middle of the street. There was no honking or complaining—the few cars simply gave him as wide a berth as possible. We stopped in front of a shop. "This is a 'Kadda' store," Doctor Srivastava told me. The Kadda stores were initiated by Gandhi and sold all sorts of objects of native craftmanship. There were numerous things of interest here, including many Indian books. I looked at one which had selections in English from the *Ocean of Story*, a huge reservoir of early narratives, perhaps legend, perhaps fiction. Finally, I purchased some beads of sandalwood, with a most delightful and enduring fragrance, and an attractive scarf.

We dropped by the guest house long enough for me to put

on a necktie—which would have been almost too much in the heat of the day. Driving back to a neighborhood close to the medical college, we stopped in front of a neat little home with a small yard. "This is where we live," Harish said simply. "It is government property, furnished to my family and to me as a faculty member."

The door opened, and a lovely picture of Indian womanhood greeted me. Mrs. Srivastava had no trace of western influence about her, either in costume or manner. She was dressed in the traditional sari and the headdress, or *usnisa*. As we entered the pleasant living room, a little girl came up and greeted me without fear or affectation. A shy little boy, of about three years, stood to one side. He wore still the long, braided hair, and his name was Siddish.

As we sat down, I noticed the pictures on the walls: a college picture of Harish; a wedding picture, and one of the Indian goddess of learning, portrayed with her musical instrument. Mrs. Srivastava had disappeared and now returned with a kind of sweet drink for us. We talked about the teaching of the medical sciences. "I suppose," said Srivastava, "that I was influenced toward my own profession largely by the fact that my father was a doctor and frequently took me to the hospital and other places connected with his practice. In medical school, the two years' anatomy course did not seem to satisfy all of my desires to know the human body thoroughly. I wanted to do more dissection and to learn the subject of anatomy in more detail. Of course, the teacher under whom I worked for the degree of Master in Surgery was himself an inspiring anatomist."

"What did you think," I asked him, "of the common tendency in America to reduce the amount of time devoted to anatomy in our medical curriculum?"

"Perhaps I should not criticize," he replied, "but I do believe that anatomy is the fundamental basis of medicine. In my opinion also," he added, "anatomy should be taught, at least at first, as pure science rather than as applied to clinical medicine."

Dinner was ready. As we sat about the table, I was somewhat curious about what was coming. This was my very first meal

FIGURE 34 Figure of the Indian goddess of learning, Sarasvati, holding
a musical instrument, the vina.

in a Hindu household. I am sorry to say that I cannot name
many of the dishes which were served. There was okra, potatoes
and rice. All of the dishes were vegetable, although several of
them could have passed for some type of meat. One dish consisted of what looked like giant almonds, another was a curdlike

white substance, and another was a yellowish "milk-sweet,"
which served as dessert. As we finished our food, and before
the coffee was served, we moved back to the living room. Harish
brought out a fine-looking motion picture projector. The white
wall made an adequate screen.

"I thought that I would show you a few scenes—some which
you are not so likely to see in ordinary films," my friend said.
The first shots were of visits to temples in various parts of India,
vacation trips and yet, to some extent, pilgrimages which the
family had made. "One great temple," Doctor Srivastava told
me, "had been attacked seventeen times by the Moguls and
defended successfully as many times by the Hindus."

Now the scenes shifted to pictures of family life: small girls
dancing; two wedding scenes, in which an exchange of garlands
was a significant part, then fireworks for the celebration of a
holiday, and finally some very gay scenes in which the merry-
makers had red powder all over their faces and clothes. In a
quieter part of this sequence we also saw Srivastava's father
and mother.

Once, while Mrs. Srivastava was out of the room, I commented
on her grace and beauty. "You may be interested to know,"
Harish told me, "that I never once had seen her until the marriage arrangement had been completed. Almost all of that was
taken care of by my sister!"

After the films, I was presented with two gifts. One was the
beautiful figure of the goddess of learning which is reproduced
here (Fig. 34) and the other was a calendar holder, made again
of the fragrant sandalwood.

When I commented on the musical instrument which the
goddess held, Srivastava told me that it is the common *vina*.
"Would you like to hear one?" he asked. "My wife is not a bad
player." A large instrument, apparently exactly the same as the
ancient one held by the goddess, was brought out and placed
on the floor. Mrs. Srivastava knelt and began to play. It was a
wholly new musical experience for me and a very pleasant one.
But while his mother played on this typically Indian device,
little Siddish sat in another part of the room listening to the

soft, tinkling tune of a Swiss music box! After the music, we talked for a while longer and I learned that my friend's father-in-law was a teacher of Sanskrit. Mrs. Srivastava was well acquainted with the work of Max Müller, that great Sanskrit scholar who had worked at Oxford University.

A car now called for me, and I was carried back to the guest house. My mind filled with the images of the day, I lay under the mosquito netting and was soon soundly asleep.

※ ※ ※

Next day I breakfasted on dry cornflakes, two fresh-fried eggs and black coffee. Shortly after nine o'clock, Srivastava arrived. With him was Doctor Patel, a demonstrator in the department of anatomy. We had arranged for a visit to the Central Institute for Ayurvedic Medicine.

What is *ayurveda*? The modern books describing this science speak of it also as *charama sastra*. Either name is meant to indicate the supreme life science, one based on all fields of knowledge that deal with the body, mind, intellect and soul of man. The ayurvedic physician, these books tell us, should be conversant with all such areas of knowledge. To most of us in the West, however, if we have heard the name at all, *ayurveda* means the system of medicine of ancient India. The purpose of the Central Institute for Ayurvedic Medicine, as set up by the Government of India, is to preserve the ancient knowledge and traditions but not to do so in a slavish manner, rather, to study these methods in the light of more recently acquired knowledge and to make fair comparisons.

At the Institute I soon learned that the two groups, the ayurvedic and the modern, actually are largely separate. We went first to the office of the ayurvedic group. Here we were greeted by the group director and his associates with the typical Hindu salutation, the hands in prayer position and the courteous bow. Then we went on to the office of the modern medicine group, where we were greeted with handshakes in western style.

After a visit to the laboratory of pathology, we entered the plant room. The bearded and turbaned ayurvedic physician in charge here was very proud and enthusiastic about the collection, which consisted not only of dried specimens but also of an extensive garden of living specimens just beyond the doors of the laboratory. I was very much interested to see that all plants were identified not only with their Latin names but also by Sanskrit ones. I was surprised at the presence of some of the more common ones, such as the sunflower. The ayurvedic scientist explained, "According to our belief, *all* plants have some medicinal power. It is there if only we will seek for it." I congratulated him on the work of which he was so obviously proud, and we continued into the hospital wards.

The hospital areas of the institute were not unusual, except that individual cases had been assigned specifically to the ayurvedic or to the modern medicine group, although cooperation and comparison were the bywords.

As I was signing the guest book, I noted the signature of none other than Pandit Nehru. He had added a very complimentary comment on the work of the institute. I noted also the signature of Charles Leslie of Pomona College, Claremont, California, my companion of the Bombay airport bus.

I was informed that the degree in ayurvedic medicine is the B.A.M.S. (Bachelor of Ayurvedic Medicine and Surgery) and that the course requires four-and-one-half years.

Doctors Srivastava and Patel and I now drove over a short distance to a large and beautifully constructed building. "This," Srivastava told me, "is the Ayurvedic College. It was founded by the Maharajah of Gujarat some years ago and is very well supported."

We entered the building and walked along the wide halls. There was an excellent modern type of auditorium, with seats for many hundreds of students and a large balcony. From here we went to the department of anatomy. It was interesting to me to observe that the anatomical studies here seemed about as practical as in our medical schools. Crocks containing various organs were standing about the laboratory. As we stepped outside, onto a shaded veranda, we encountered a group of students bent over a human liver and comparing it with an illustration in a textbook. And what was the textbook? Why, *Cun-*

ningham, the one which we were using at the time in my own department!

Back in another of the spacious hallways, we stopped before an extremely large mural. It depicted a conclave of sages in the foothills of the Himalaya Mountains. The description below it informed me that this was a gathering which took place in 2000 B.C. in the "propitious environment of the slopes of the Himalayas," a meeting at which some of the main tenets of ayurveda had been laid down. Here, then, I thought, I am looking at the scene of perhaps the earliest "medical convention" of which there is any record.

We left the college, passing a few cows pasturing peacefully on its grounds, drove a short distance and stopped in front of a rather weird-looking structure, a towerlike affair with a glassed-in summit. "This is the solarium," my friend explained. "It was invented by a Frenchman, Doctor Saidman. Its only counterpart is in France." There were several floors. On one of them we saw instruments for measurement of intensity of the sunlight and, as my friend said, "for measurement of the sensitivity of the skin of different individuals." On the uppermost floor, which was designed to *rotate* by means of an intricate mechanism (I suppose not unlike those for telescopes in observatories) were a series of rooms with beds which could be tilted to catch the sunlight at special angles. Here the patient being treated either for skin diseases or general conditions could receive controlled doses of sunlight over given periods of time. Downstairs we visited the baths and saw more equipment for various types of treatments. The physical therapist in charge had been at the tower for nine years. He showed us many before and after pictures of persons who had benefitted from treatments there.

This visit to the solarium was an experience wholly unexpected by me and was of much interest in representing somewhat of a bypath in the history of medical treatment and therapeutic technique. We now went directly to the M. P. Shad Medical School. In the administrative office, I met Doctor P. P. Seth, F.R.C.S., who was acting dean at this time, in the absence of Doctor Joseph, the dean of the school. When I learned that

Seth was retired (I believe that he was under sixty years of age) I commented on the fact which I had noted before of the apparently early retirement age in India. "Well," said Seth, with a twinkle in his eye, "there probably are two main reasons for it: first, we feel that one must 'make way' for the upcoming generation, and second, many people here think that the brain stops working at about my age."

Doctor Srivastava now took me on visits to the various departments. The laboratories of physiology were not unlike those in which I had worked in graduate school and medical school. The smoked paper drums (kymographs) for recording muscle contraction, were much in evidence. In many schools in America they now have been replaced by an electronic apparatus known as the Offner recorder. In the physiology department, there were separate rooms for studies on basal metabolism, electroencephalography and other subjects.

In the biochemistry department, the professor was a man who had been at Michigan State University in East Lansing for three years and had obtained his Ph.D there. His researches at Jamnagar had been chiefly on the thyroid gland and its secretion. A considerable proportion of his time, he told me, was spent, however, in doing alcohol analyses. India, since prohibition was instituted there, has had a difficult task in controlling traffic in alcohol. "Almost every type of bottle," he said, "is used in a masquerade to transport alcohol." He showed me a glass case filled with bottles of many shapes and sizes, and with diverse labels, all of which had been found to contain alcohol or alcoholic beverages of different kinds when analyzed in his laboratory. "One not infrequent way of carrying containers of alcohol," he told us "is the 'pregnant woman' dodge in which as many containers can be transported as can be concealed under the garments of a lady who really is not pregnant at all."

We went on next to the department of anatomy. In the gross anatomy laboratory, I saw another of the dried mummies. My friend commented, "A mummy makes a very fine 'human blackboard' for locating landmarks, lines of position and location of organs." The gross anatomy laboratory was a busy place. Two years were allotted to the study of anatomy at Jamnagar. Not only was there much time for dissection and for topographic anatomy, but a Siemens machine from the German company of that name was used for radiological studies of the normal human body. We spent some time in the anatomical museum. A number of the specimens here were in museum jars imported from Czechoslovakia.

We next went downstairs to visit the department of pathology. Here the biopsies were studied and all the surgical material was handled, as well as the tissue from autopsies. Also, as in the majority of institutions in our country, clinical chemistry work was carried out here. The training of technicians both for clinical chemistry and tissue preparations was an important part of the departmental function.

A feature of the M. P. Shah Medical College which seemed to me admirable, and even to some extent luxurious, is the fact that each department occupies a complete floor and has its own lecture room, museum and departmental library area on that floor.

I was now taken back to the guest house where I was to stay until late afternoon, then to return to the medical school and in the evening to give my lecture there.

At lunch I met a charming gentleman, a Mr. Menon. He remarked, "I have just come up from Bombay—by train, of course—I would never fly during the monsoon season!" Mr. Menon came from Kerala, a state much in the news because of the strength there of the Communist party. He told me that the name "Menon" is a common one in the South and "Patel" a common one in the North, including Gujarat. We talked about the regional language problem, which is a very real thing in India and which has been a cause of bloody riots. "At the present time," I was told, "there is a strong effort to have the textbooks in our schools published in *Gujarati* rather than in Hindi or English—but I do not think that it can succeed." We talked about the food. His English was very good except for one word, which always came out "potitoes." He told me that the Jains, who are numerous in Gujarat, will never eat at the same table with non-Jains. As I rose and left the room, I had a little sample of exclusiveness. A bearded and turbaned man very carefully avoided entering by the door through which I was leaving, and went out of his way to use a different one!

I spent a half hour arranging my lantern slides and notes, then took a brief rest during the heat of the day. At about four o'clock Doctor Srivastava and Doctor Patel arrived, and we returned to the medical school. In the departmen of pharmacology we met the professor, who was a very impressive-looking Sikh with a light pink turban and excellent strength and regularity of features. I enjoyed the visit in the laboratories here even more than in some of the other departments. The students were studying the effects of perfusions with various drugs, using a huge frog, similar to our bullfrogs. In the pharmacology museum—a combination of words sounding strange to medical scientists of the West, I saw many dried plants, including the 'foxglove' from which digitalis is obtained, and was reminded that these blossoms really are glove-shaped. Here too we saw the seeds of the colcichum, the source of the alkaloid colchicine, used in treatment of gout.

In this department many excellent portraits hung on the walls. Here was Selman Waksman, Nobel prize winner in 1952 for his work on isolation of new antibiotics, including actomycin and streptomycin. There also was a fine picture of the great experimental pathologist, Geheimrat Ehrlich, taken in 1911.

It was time now for tea. We went into a conference room where some twenty persons were gathered at a long table. Apparently almost all of the faculty were here. Conversation soon flowed freely. Much of it was as light as under similar circumstances in America. There were some reminiscences. One of the anatomists had been at the great battle of Imphal in World War II and told of his exciting experiences. After tea we all went out to a broad terrace, from which the view of Jamnagar, with its towers and temples, lay before us. I saw what looked like a large tent in the distance and asked about it. "Why, that is a circus," one of the faculty told me. "We have many travelling circuses here."

As we left the medical school, Srivastava asked me if I would like to visit a Jain temple. I was eager to do so. We drove along

a relatively quiet street. At the doors of the temple, the three of us
were met by a slender young attendant. He asked us to remove
our shoes and socks. Barefooted, we entered a cool and dark
chamber. A fragrance of strange incense filled the air as we
walked slowly over the marble floor. The room in which we were
was not a large one, perhaps fifty feet long and half as wide, but
the atmosphere reminded me very much of that in a cathedral.
The walls were covered with elaborate pictures in relief, mainly
of other temples and of religious compounds in various parts of
India. The scenes were brightened by large amounts of gold
leaf decorating the temples and avenues. At the far end of the
chamber was a sort of inner sanctum with a glass front. In the
dimly lighted interior of this sanctum we could see three human
figures, life sized and very lifelike. The eyes were of some material which had a remarkable power of reflecting the light. The
effect was not only an impressive but, at least to me, an eerie one.

We left the chamber by a side door and, outside again in the
bright sunlight, ascended some stone stairs. At their top, the
attendant pointed out a part of the original structure, about 400
years old, around which the new temple had been built. Still
visible on it were some fine elephant carvings. In an upstairs
room of the new temple we saw some small but exquisitely made
idols.

"Perhaps you would like to know" the attendant said, and
Doctor Srivastava was the interpreter, "that there are two different sects of Jains. In the one, the priests believe in wearing a
loin cloth, in the other, they wear nothing."

Back in the lower chamber, I noticed in a recess in the wall a
marvellous model—a city in miniature with the most finely constructed buildings glittering with gold and jewels. My friends told
me that it was a representation of one of the heavenly cities.
What a wealth of imagination, of reverence and perhaps of super-
stition, I thought, was to be found in this great religion of which
most westerners know nothing whatsoever—not even its name!

We returned to the guest house, and after a light dinner there,
I picked up the inevitable notes and slides for the lecture.

It was a very warm evening. As we entered the large auditorium, there was no cooling solace of air-conditioning. There was, however, a tremendous applause, but this time, after my experience in Bombay, I was more prepared for it.

The talk itself seemed to be received with good attention. Some of my lantern slides had to be maneuvered to make them fit the projector. At the close of the talk there was a discussion in which Doctor Seth and others took part. At this time also I was really surprised to meet a young man who had taken his M.S. degree in our school of dentistry in 1959. He was Mr. Navin Desai, and, of course, he was eager to send his best wishes to the dean of the school, Doctor Maynard K. Hine, and to others of the faculty.

It was a good evening, but a *very* warm one, and after one final cup of tea at the guest house, I turned in and fell into a somewhat fitful sleep.

In the morning I had my early tea followed by a breakfast of fried eggs and coffee. The time was made more interesting by another conversation with Mr. Menon of Kerala. He was complaining about the difficulties of really getting down to business in many places where he visited. "With all of the tea drinking and chewing of chupan, every little negotiation can be dragged out for hours," he said. "But, well, after all, we are known as a hospitable people."

As I completed packing, I learned that Mr. Gosh of the Tax Division would be moving into the room which I had occupied.

Out in the lobby, where I sat down to wait for my friend, there were people gathering and many cups being set out. I learned that it was the beginning of the "tree plantation" celebration, and I shared in it to the extent of having another cup of tea. Suddenly the man in the chair next to mine leaned toward me and said, "Doctor Andrew, I heard your lecture last evening." It gave me a feeling of belonging in this group. My new acquaintance was an aviation engineer. I could see that this guest house really would be a good place to spend some days or weeks to have a look at a cross section of the governmental and business people of modern India.

Shortly afterwards, Doctor Srivastava arrived. It was only a short distance over to the Air India Office, and we walked in this cooler morning air. My baggage was loaded carefully onto a horse-drawn buggy. We set out through the relatively quiet streets of this part of Jamnagar. But the events of the trip were not quite over, for coming down the middle of the street before us were five beautiful elephants, with their attendant. There really was nothing unusual about the scene—they were probably work animals; but it seemed to help to round out my stay.

At the door of the airport bus my friend said goodbye. He hoped to see me again in India, but if his plans went well, he would be a professor in the larger city of Baroda soon. A lively bus ride over a road shared with oxen, donkeys and camels took us to the airport. In the large waiting room I sat and watched the many birds which came in through open doors and windows. I asked about a particularly striking one with a green ring about each eye, but the only names that I could obtain were in Telegu and in Gujarati. I noticed that the small group of persons was waiting with a general cheerfulness and a seeming lack of impatience.

Now our plane was ready to take off for the long trip: first to Bombay; then to Teheran; Cairo; Rome; and London, and finally, home! My days on this visit to Jamnagar had been filled with the sights and sounds of India—this ancient land still so fascinating, so varied and so mysterious. But most vivid in my mind as I began the journey home were the warm and friendly faces of my Indian hosts.

INDEX

A

Advani, 224, 225, 227
Aedes aegypti mosquito, as carrier of
  yellow fever, 6
Aging, *See also* Gerontology
  acceptance as field of scientific
    study, 53, 54
  study of with funds from U. S.
    Public Health Service, 61-62
  theory autointoxication as cause of,
    57, 62
Ahmed, Basheer, 210
American Association of Anatomists, 86
Amsterdam, Holland
  Royal Tropical Institute, 100-101,
    104-106
  tile from 18th century home, photo-
    graph, 100
  transportation in, 100-101
  trip to, 96, 98-99
  Victoria Hotel, 99
Anatomy, faces of, 126
Andreas, Carl, 198
Andrew, Nancy, 16, 17, 24, 43, 66, 83,
    87, 102, 103
Andrew, Warren, 2, 18, 162, 256
  books by in Fujita's library, 162
  photograph, 2
Anopheles Abu-manus mosquito
  as carrier of malarian protozoan, 8
  food of, 8-9
  shape of, 8
  study of, 8-9
Apollo Bunder, 227
Argentina
  Buenos Aires, *See* Buenos Aires
  Institute of Biology and Experimental
    Medicine, Buenos Aires, 78-79
  model figures from, photograph, 80
  National University of, Buenos Aires,
    77-78

Arjuna, 243
Ashmore, James, 203, 212
Asoka Pillars, 231, 232
Asoka-vardhana, 232
Ayurveda, definition, 249
Ayurvedic College, Jamnagar, India
  department of anatomy, 250-251
  description, 250-251
  founding of, 250
  solarium of, 251

B

Bachmann, Carl, 196
Bacon, George B., 185
Bacon, Roger, 55
Badano-Repeto, 27
Bangkok, Thailand
  description, 182-184
  hand-carved teakwood elephant, pho-
    tograph, 189
  Marble Temple, 183-184
  Obosot, 193
  Temple of the Dawn, 196-197
  Temple of the Emerald Buddha, 192-
    193
  trip to, 180
  welcome to, 181
Barr, Murray, 91
Basel, Switzerland, distinctions of city,
    177
Basic Medical Science Institute in Pak-
    istan, 198, 201
Bennett, Miss, 88
Bensley, Robert R., 15, 26, 116
  pioneer work in physical methods of
    cytology, 15
Bergman, R. A. M., 96, 97, 98, 99, 100,
    101, 102, 103, 104, 105, 106, 107,
    108, 109, 110, 111, 112
  ambitions of, 108
  as Professor of Anthropology, 98